C000099803

FOR BREW
FREAKS,
BEAN
GEEKS,
AND
THE
SIMPLY
CURIOUS ...

THE NORTH
AND NORTH WALES
INDEPENDENT

COFFEE
GUIDE

the INSIDER'S GUIDE TO SPECIALITY
COFFEE VENUES AND ROASTERS

★ ★ ★ ★ ★ ★ ★ ★ ★ ★

№ 3

Salt Media, 5 Cross Street, Devon, EX31 1BA.
www.saltmedia.co.uk
Tel: 01271 859299
Email: ideas@saltmedia.co.uk

Salt Media *Independent Coffee Guide* team:
Nick Cooper, Lucy Deasy, Kathryn Lewis, Abi Manning,
Lisa McNeil, Fi Mason, Tamsin Powell, Jo Rees,
James Roberts, Rosanna Rothery, Emma Scott-Goldstone,
Christopher Sheppard, Dale Stiling, Katie Taylor,
Mark Tibbles, Ella Townsend and Harry Wild.
Design and illustration: Salt Media

**A big thank you to the *Independent Coffee Guide*
committee** (meet them on page 188) for their
expertise and enthusiasm, **our headline sponsors**
Cimbali, KeepCup and Schluter, **and sponsors** Bunn,
Cakesmiths, Frobishers, Atkinsons and
Stephensons Dairy.

Coffee shops, cafes and roasters are invited to be
included in the guide based on meeting criteria set by
the committee, which includes a high quality coffee
experience for visitors, use of speciality beans and
being independently run.

For information on the Ireland, Scottish, and South West
and South Wales *Independent Coffee Guides,* visit:

www.indycoffee.guide
🐦 @indycoffeeguide
📷 @indycoffeeguide

CONTENTS

Double Espresso 1.8
Macchiato 1.9
Cappuccino (8 oz) 2.2
Flat White (7 oz) 2.30
Latte (10 oz) 2.40
Mocha (10 oz) 2.40
Americano (8 oz) 2.10
Iced Latte (10 oz) 2.40
Aeropress Filter 2.20
Real Hot Chocolate 2.40
Loose Leaf Teas from 2.10

> BREW & BROWNIE №63

Welcome to the third edition of the *The North and North Wales Independent Coffee Guide*, our biggest yet and my first as editor.

As you follow the guide across the North, you'll discover a clan of new cafes and coffee shops serving carefully crafted, locally roasted coffee, alongside institutions which have been flying the flag for speciality since the early days.

It's this open-minded and welcoming culture which makes coffee such an incredible industry to be a part of. It's not always been easy though, as we discover in our feature on speciality's northern trailblazers on page 12. You'll also find some of the region's newest finds in our Tour de Speciality feature on page 30.

To reflect the rise of roasteries flinging open their doors to coffee-curious members of the public, we've included them within the regional areas in this edition. So next time you're sipping a roasted-down-the-road brew, check to see if you can swing by the roastery for a natter and to pick up a bag for the road.

We'd love to hear how you get on coffee shop hopping across this caffeine-rich region. Hit us up with your latest snaps and finds on Instagram and Twitter.

Kathryn Lewis
Editor
Indy Coffee Guides

🐦 @indycoffeeguide
📷 @indycoffeeguide

PIONEERING SPIRITS

MEET THE TRAILBLAZERS WHO BROUGHT SPECIALITY COFFEE TO THE NORTH

With the nation's thirst for speciality coffee seemingly unquenchable, it's hard to believe that just ten years ago you'd be lucky to sniff out a good cup in London, let alone in the rest of the UK. A decade later and the North's quality caffeine culture is booming, thanks to a small group of trailblazers who were the first to fly the flag for speciality. We extract tales of blood, sweat and tampers from some of the industry's northern pioneers.

JOE MEAGHER

'I'd decided to pursue a career in coffee before I was made redundant,' explains Joe Meagher, founder of Newcastle's Flat Caps Coffee. 'The financial crash just happened to hit at the right time for me.'

'I didn't know what was going down in Melbourne or London; I just wanted to run my own business where quality produce was at the heart of the operation.

'At first I had visions of an old-school coffee shop with pick 'n' mix style beans lining the walls but as soon as I started doing a bit of research and training with local roaster Pumphreys I decided to focus on speciality.

'When Flat Caps opened in a basement on Ridley Place in 2010, no one else was doing speciality in Newcastle. Money didn't stretch to a sign for the first six months and the loyal following that the cafe quickly garnered was purely down to word of mouth.

'MONEY DIDN'T STRETCH TO A SIGN FOR THE FIRST SIX MONTHS'

'After six years Flat Caps outgrew its original home and, following a successful crowdfunding campaign, relocated to a bigger space. Taking on a former coffee shop has given us the opportunity to meet new customers who may not have been interested in speciality before.

'The coffee community is now thriving in Newcastle and although it's great to see more shops popping up, we can't keep dividing our customers. There's a strong foodie culture here and I believe that introducing those who are passionate about quality ingredients to quality coffee will be the key to broadening the market.'

IAN STEEL

ATKINSONS, LANCASTER

'WE DON'T MIND HAVING OUR IDEAS RIPPED OFF BECAUSE THEY ALWAYS MUTATE INTO SOMETHING PERSONAL TO EACH VENUE'

'As longtime speciality coffee fans, it was a lightbulb moment over a 1924 Cona Table Model syphon that decided Sue [Ian's wife] and my career move into coffee in 2005,' says Ian Steel of Atkinsons.

'Eight months after asking the previous owners of Atkinsons whether they'd ever thought of selling the business, we'd left our dream family home, downsized to a cottage and had the keys to our very own roastery.

'At first the longstanding customers told us not to change a thing, though it wasn't long before we grew in confidence and started to progress into speciality coffee.

'Opening The Music Room in 2010 was another important step; introducing third wave coffee to a small market town was certainly an eye-opener for its residents. Social seating was another game-changer. Initially, some customers avoided the communal benches like the plague, but now they're always full at both The Hall and The Music Room.

'We've seen some fantastic startups open around us. Though some are a little similar, we don't mind having our ideas ripped off because they always mutate into something personal to each venue and its owners.

'As a wiser man than I once said: "There's no progress without change".'

DAVE OLEJNIK

LAYNES ESPRESSO, LEEDS

'MY HURDLE WAS TO CONVINCE A CITY OF 750,000 THAT BUYING A COFFEE OF THIS SIZE, STYLE AND PRICE WAS A GOOD THING'

'It was coffee shop hopping while touring as a guitar technician that inspired me to open my own cafe on my return to Leeds in 2009,' explains Dave Olejnik, owner of Laynes Espresso in Leeds.

'After finding the perfect spot I started talking business loans with banks but the economic climate in 2010 made it really difficult. In the end I took out a whopping personal loan which certainly put the pressure on to make it work.

'Lou Henry at Opposite had already laid down the speciality foundations in the city with her stand in the Victoria Quarter. My hurdle was to convince a city of 750,000 that buying a coffee of this size, style and price was a good thing. It was tough, but social media was a huge help in spreading the word.

'Six years later, Leeds' coffee scene has grown hugely. Shops are opening in suburban areas and it's inspiring to see speciality reaching people in their local communities.'

ALEX GALANTINO

LA BOTTEGA MILANESE, LEEDS

'We opened La Bottega Milanese in November 2009 during the longest spell of heavy snow the North had seen in 20 years,' says owner Alex Galantino. 'We took roughly £700 in our first week and spent most days helping people off the pavements.

'PEOPLE OPENING SPECIALITY SHOPS NOW HAVE IT A HELLUVA LOT EASIER'

'Once the snow had melted and footfall increased, we received the anticipated complaints – size, temperature of milk, lack of syrups – but eventually we carved out an audience through patience and focus. Luckily Leeds is very supportive of indie businesses and we became "the coffee shop to try down by the river".

'People opening speciality shops now have it a helluva lot easier, as the original pioneers have done the leg work in opening up the market. Having said that, increasing rates and rents may see the future of speciality move to the suburbs.

'For a long time there were only three shops in Leeds serving great coffee; now we have one of the most vibrant scenes outside of London.'

WAYNE & JANE LEW

NORTH TEA POWER, MANCHESTER

'In 2010 we couldn't find any cafes in Manchester preparing the type of speciality coffee we'd admired in America, Copenhagen and Berlin,' says Wayne Lew, co-owner of North Tea Power in Manchester. 'The options were corporate chain or bar; coffee was simply an afterthought.

'Hidden from the street and introducing something completely novel to the area, the first six months of North Tea Power were slow and painful for my wife Jane and me. It was branching out and making friends in the local community that helped us grow our loyal following.

'We've been branded as hipster in the past and this can really put people off. From the start, creating an inclusive and friendly environment was as important to us as the coffee offering.

'SUDDENLY EVERYWHERE SERVES SPECIALITY, FROM THE PIE SHOP TO THE PUB'

'Though speciality coffee as a brand is certainly booming – it seems that suddenly everywhere serves speciality, from the pie shop to the pub – it's incredible to see it being taken up so widely.'

JEREMY PERKINS

COFFEEVOLUTION, HUDDERSFIELD

'I set-up Coffeevolution in November 2000 and although the term "speciality coffee" had been coined in the 1970s, it was still very early days,' explains owner Jeremy Perkins.

'The biggest hurdle we encountered was education, especially 17 years ago when coffee only really stretched to Starbucks outside of London. People often reacted to our menu with sheer panic, not understanding what was on offer.

'Times have changed and although education is still a big part of what we do, our customers are very receptive to different brewing methods and are full of surprises. A cluster of coffee shops have followed suit in Huddersfield but the scene is by no means as prevalent as that in Leeds or Manchester.

'It's the general standard of coffee that needs to improve now. How many times have you been to a restaurant where the quality of food is outstanding but the experience falls short when it comes to the coffee? My hope is that speciality shops can influence other food and drink businesses to help raise the quality of coffee.'

'PEOPLE REACTED TO OUR MENU WITH SHEER PANIC'

JONATHAN PERRY

TAMPER, SHEFFIELD

'After emigrating from Auckland to Sheffield in 2011, it was sticking to our beliefs that proved hardest when we opened the original Tamper on Westfield Terrace,' says owner Jonathan Perry.

'Sheffield, like a lot of the UK, was full of high street coffee brands which do things completely differently to us. Customers' perceptions of how coffee should be served and taste differed vastly and business was slow at the start. However, we didn't compromise and, with the right staff who believed in what we were trying to do; we built a solid base of caffeine converts within a year.

'Some great coffee shops have joined us in Sheffield's speciality scene; the industry is improving and I believe this will continue. More young people aspire to become baristas now, viewing hospitality as a career rather than just a job. And with an increasing number of speciality roasters setting up across South Yorkshire, the quality will continue to improve as opinions change and understanding of coffee increases.'

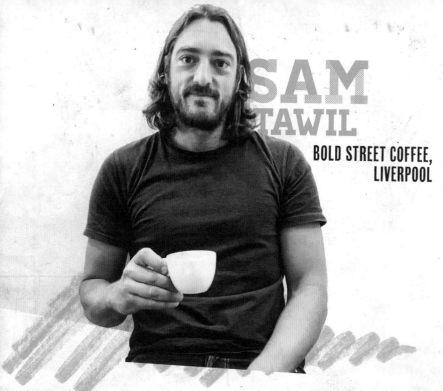

SAM TAWIL

'When we started Bold Street we had to make things accessible,' explains founder Sam Tawil. 'We were almost exclusively selling lattes in the early days but once we'd gained our regulars' trust we were able to introduce them to something more specialist.

'I'd worked in a small chain of coffee shops which were the best of the bunch in Liverpool in 2005. After that I did the festival coffee cart thing but it wasn't until 2010 that the bricks and mortar venue materialised.

'Taking over a former coffee shop helped as we already had a customer base. As the first speciality shop in the city, we didn't go out with the intention of changing the community's perception of coffee, although today we sell more filters than flat whites.

'ONCE WE'D GAINED OUR REGULARS' TRUST WE WERE ABLE TO INTRODUCE THEM TO SOMETHING MORE SPECIALIST'

'What became clear very quickly was that it's extremely difficult to make a speciality cafe a success without offering food alongside the coffee. I'm sure the scene will continue to grow in Liverpool but it will be the social spaces that can do both food and coffee well that will last.'

S30
Perfect Touch

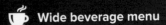 **Wide beverage menu**

 **Self adjusting grinders**

Bi-directional Wi-Fi control

LaCimbali **S30** is the new superautomatic machine created to offer up to **24 different recipes**. The grouphead design guarantees maximum reliability and consistent beverage quality, while the new milk circuit delivers hot and cold frothed milk directly to the cup.
LaCimbali **S30**, the perfect way to satisfy every taste.

reddot award 2016
winner

PRO GUIDE TO
HOME BREWING

Hankering after a perfect barista-style coffee at home? Cofficionado **Hannah Davies** of Cup North spills the beans on how to crack home brewing

DOSE

The ratio of coffee to water has a direct impact on the strength of your brew. The general rule in the UK is to use 60g of coffee per litre of water.

 You'll be able to determine the strength of a coffee by assessing the mouthfeel – is it thick on the tongue or thin with a watery texture?

WATER TEMPERATURE

The temperature of the water has a direct impact on the length of time it'll take for the coffee to be extracted. It also impacts on the flavours you'll elicit from the bean. The recommended temperature for brewing coffee is 92-96°c.

 Always preheat your brewing apparatus to maintain a consistent water temperature throughout the brew time.

MYTH BUSTER
BOILING WATER BURNS COFFEE

When you introduce boiling water to coffee, the high energy within the water extracts the kind of bitter and astringent flavours we associate with a burnt taste.

WATER QUALITY

Use filtered water from a good home filtering jug or buy bottled mineral water (look out for a neutral ph level and a dry residue close to 180).

GRIND SIZE AND FRESHNESS

For maximum flavour, be sure to grind your coffee beans just before you plan to brew. You will need to adjust the grind size depending on the brew method. Maintain a consistent dose size and water temperature, but experiment by using fine and coarse grind sizes to see how it affects the flavour. You're aiming to find the sweet spot.

TIME

For immersion brew methods like french press (cafetiere) or Clever Dripper, ensure that you time the brew from the moment the water comes into contact with the coffee. I recommend anywhere from 3-4 minutes.

For drip brew methods like V60 or Kalita, monitor the time from when you start brewing to when the water stops dripping through the bed of coffee. If it's taking too long (over 3 minutes) then consider making the grind size coarser, which allows the water to flow more freely through the coffee bed. If the water runs through in 60 seconds or less, make the grind size finer.

CONSISTENCY

Think of brewing coffee like a school science experiment: if you're unhappy with the way the coffee tastes, change just one variable at a time.

HOME BREWING

Now you're down with the brew basics, choose your weapon and refine your style

AEROPRESS

> This is a flexible brewing device. You can make the grind size coarse and brew for 3-4 minutes to recreate a french press style brew. Alternatively, grind the beans on a fine setting and brew for 30 seconds with less water to create an espresso-style drink. Have a play.

> Set up the brewer on a set of scales so you can monitor the volume of water as you pour.

IMMERSION
(FRENCH PRESS/ CLEVER DRIPPER)

> Avoid inconsistency in the brew caused by stirring (or not) the coffee and water. Stirring one time and not the next will alter the extraction of the coffee so you can't tell what's working.

> Set up the brewer on a set of scales so you can monitor the volume of water as you pour.

POUROVER
(V60/KALITA)

> Wet the filter paper in the brewer before you start. This helps to reduce any potential papery taste and warms up the brewer.

> Use a dose of coffee and water relative to the size of the brewer – the bed of coffee should be 2-3cm deep.

> Bloom the coffee. This means adding a small amount of water (2 x dose of coffee) to the fresh grounds when you start the timer and letting the coffee release gases for approximately 30 seconds before adding the remainder of the water.

> Set up the brewer on a set of scales so you can monitor the volume of water as you pour.

> Invest in a kettle with a long spout which encourages a slow and controlled pour.

KEEPCUP.COM

REUSABLE

— NOT —

DISPOSABLE

MILK OF HUMAN KINDNESS

You know exactly where your coffee came from – often down to the coffee farmer's name – and you're satisfied that a fair price was tendered for those locally roasted beans. So why ignore the milk?

According to Steph Stephenson, if you're going to talk about the provenance, flavour and quality of coffee beans, it makes sense to use ethically sourced, free-range milk.

'Why go to all that effort with the coffee then pour in any old milk?' asks Steph, who runs Stephensons Dairy in Morecambe near Lancaster with husband Chris. Together they've created the first dairy to launch free-range milk in the UK.

Not all milk is the same, Steph tells us.

'Most people presume that all cows live outside, roaming romantically on lush green pastures, but sadly that's far from the truth.'

'Pressure on farms to join the ruthless competition for cheap milk has turned the dairy industry into an intensive factory farming operation, where cows seldom go outside and are typically fed Total Mixed Rations (TMR) which is a mix of maize, wheat, rapeseed and GM soya.'

Steph and Chris are on a mission to change that, by collaborating with farmers who are committed to grazing cows outdoors for a minimum of 180 days and nights each year.

'The North has a great climate for growing grass, and cows are inquisitive and social creatures that are born to forage and graze,' she says. *'Allowing them the freedom of the fields lets them express their natural behaviour and enjoy the diet they were designed to eat as ruminants.'*

Looking out for the Pasture Promise logo is one way to ensure that the foamy top on your flat white can be traced from field to fridge, and it's a symbol that's gaining recognition in the quality coffee scene.

'Not only are speciality coffee shops using free-range milk for its great taste, they also like the fact that the milk provides local farmers with a sustainable future,' adds Steph.

Some baristas believe it's the healthier option for their customers, too.

'Increasingly, evidence shows that milk produced from cows that graze, compared to those fed a diet high in grain, is lower in saturated fat and contains more healthy fats like omega-3,' says Steph.

All well and good, but how does it rate as a canvas?

'Baristas love our milk,' smiles Steph. 'Not only does it taste delicious, it also performs beautifully when steamed, so is ideal for creating latte art.'

'BARISTAS LIKE THE FACT THAT OUR MILK PROVIDES LOCAL FARMERS WITH A SUSTAINABLE FUTURE'

Tour de SPECIALITY

WITH NEW SPECIALITY SHOPS CROPPING UP ACROSS THE NORTH AND PIONEER ROASTERS FLINGING OPEN THEIR DOORS TO COFFEE FANS, THERE'S NEVER BEEN A BETTER TIME FOR A CAFFEINE-FUELLED ROAD TRIP

The City Tour

Get your urban cafe fix with a coffee tour of **Leeds**, **Manchester** and **Sheffield**

THE ROUTE

Fresh from the train in ⇌ LEEDS, make tracks to the newly extended LAYNES ESPRESSO for a European tour of speciality roasters, or head south from the station to OUT OF THE WOODS for Dark Woods espresso and rustic fodder. Whichever direction you take next – dockside to THE GRUB AND GROG SHOP or into town for nitro thrills at KAPOW COFFEE – you'll soon hit something specialist.

In ⇌ MANCHESTER, take in the coffee houses with a tram tour across the city, making stops at GRINDSMITH ESPRESSO & BREWBAR on Deansgate for filter gear geek-outs, and FEDERAL CAFE & BAR on Nicholas Croft for an Antipodean brunch sesh. Or mosey over to the creative Northern Quarter for a swift espresso and cheese toastie at TAKK.

Start your reccie 'round ⇌ SHEFFIELD with an Instagramable brekkie at MARMADUKES CAFE DELI followed by a mid-morning speciality hit at TAMPER-WESTFIELD TERRACE. Afternoon indulgences can be taken in the form of cascara tonics and peanut butter and jam doughnuts at UPSHOT on Glossop Road.

💼 **PACKING ESSENTIALS** Without sounding like your mother, pack a sturdy pair of shoes. That step count will quickly rack up.

📷 **FUEL THE JOURNEY** Speciality doesn't stop at 5pm. In Manchester, POT KETTLE BLACK's badass brunch plates can be plundered 'til 7pm, while authentic Italian lasagne and flat breads are available until close at LA BOTTEGA MILANESE-BOND COURT in Leeds. In Sheffield, head to TAMPER-SELLERS WHEEL for Friday night thrills.

EASE 7/10

THIS WILL TAKE A FEW DAYS, BUT WHAT A TRIP. WE'D RECOMMEND TAKING THE TRAIN AS EVERYWHERE IS WITHIN WALKING DISTANCE.

The Lakes Tour

Make like Steve Coogan and Rob Brydon and do your own version of *The Trip* – but with coffee and cheese toasties instead of Michelin starred fine dining

THE ROUTE

Start at the charming town of Kirkby Lonsdale and visit Anthony at KIRCABI roastery. Don't expect the usual industrial premises: this is a quaint little store in the centre of town where you can see roasting in action while grabbing a coffee to-go. Suitably buzzing, whizz through to Staveley where you'll find MORE? THE ARTISAN BAKERY for slabs of traybake cake and stonking gourmet sausage rolls.

Just around the corner, Stephen at MR DUFFIN'S COFFEE is also great to visit; sit in the cafe while he cooks up coffee beans in front of you.

HOMEGROUND COFFEE & KITCHEN in Windermere takes the biscuit for a drool-worthy brunch or lunch, along with cracking homemade cakes and coffee from Lakes roaster, CARVETII.

PACKING ESSENTIALS Travel *The Trip* style by Mini, with a simple overnight bag slung in the boot and a copy of the *Indy Coffee Guide*. Don't forget to brush up on your Al Pacino impression beforehand.

FUEL THE JOURNEY You'll find a few good farm shops en route, so if you really can't wait for your next chow down, grab some local goodies. Give the Kendal mint cake a miss though – a sugar hit of that proportion with your caffeine intake will tip you over the edge.

EASE 8/10

A BIT OF PLANNING IS REQUIRED, PLUS A VEHICLE, AND IT WOULD BE A SHAME NOT TO STAY THE NIGHT AND DO IT AT A LEISURELY PACE.

North Eastern Tour

Take a caffeinated trip across the North's eastern edge and discover incredible coffee and coastal seascapes

THE ROUTE

Kick off close to the Scottish border with a trip to PILGRIMS COFFEE on Holy Island for a cup of the tidal isle's namesake brew. Heading south, make a pit-stop on the outskirts of Newcastle for fabulous filters at BLK COFFEE in Heaton before brunching at HARVEST's Jesmond joint.

Continue skimming the coast to BEDFORD ST COFFEE in Middlesbrough – this is the original cafe from the guys at Rounton Coffee – then motor across country to sample the killer scones at MINT HOBO in Yarm.

Finally, saunter down to Scarborough for a day of sun, sea and speciality with an excursion to YAY COFFEE! on York Place and to try the new kid on the coffee block, GREENSMITH & THACKWRAY.

PACKING ESSENTIALS A good road map, a couple of bottles of cold brew – Yorkshire's ARTEMIS is a great shout – for the journey and some factor 30 sun cream (hope springs eternal).

FUEL THE JOURNEY Stock up on hearty slices of homemade cake at each stop to see you through to the next caffeine hit.

EASE 7/10
A LITTLE FORWARD PLANNING WOULD BE USEFUL BUT HEY, THAT'S WHAT THE SATNAV IS FOR.

www.schlutercoffee.com
E: liverpool@schluter.ch
T: +44 (0)151 498 6500

SCHLUTER

SINCE 1858

Speciality green coffee suppliers

—— since 1858 ——

Purpose.
Passion.
Progress.

HOW TO USE THE GUIDE

> MR DUFFIN'S COFFEE –
THE COFFEE DEN №35

CAFES

Coffee shops and cafes where you can drink
top-notch speciality coffee. We've split the guide into
areas to help you find places near you.

ROASTERS

Meet the leading speciality coffee roasters in the North
and discover where to source beans to use at home.
Find them after the cafes in each area.

MAPS

Every cafe and roastery has a number so you can
find them either on the area map at the start of each
section, or on the detailed city maps.

MORE GOOD STUFF

Discover MORE GOOD CUPS and MORE GOOD ROASTERS at the back
of the book.

WWW.INDYCOFFEE.GUIDE

**Don't forget to let us know how you get on as you
explore the best speciality cafes and roasteries**

🐦 @indycoffeeguide 📷 @indycoffeeguide

THE ADVENTURE STARTS HERE

> GREENSMITH & THACKWRAY №59

NORTHUMBERLAND, TYNE AND WEAR & COUNTY DURHAM

> FLAT CAPS COFFEE №6

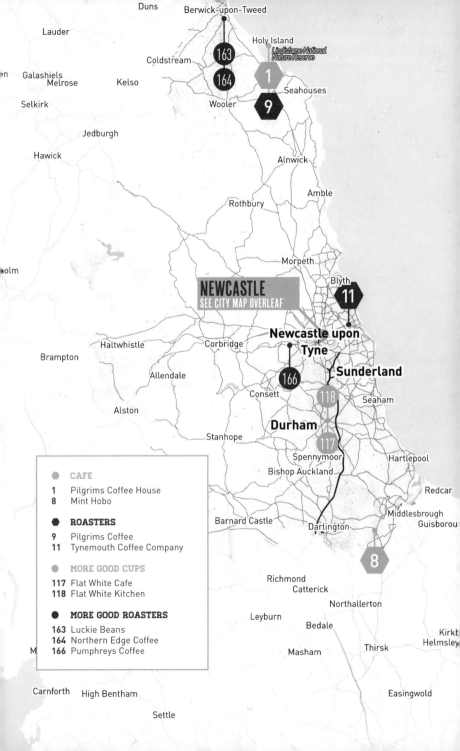

NEWCASTLE
SEE CITY MAP OVERLEAF

CAFE
1   Pilgrims Coffee House
8   Mint Hobo

ROASTERS
9   Pilgrims Coffee
11 Tynemouth Coffee Company

MORE GOOD CUPS
117 Flat White Cafe
118 Flat White Kitchen

MORE GOOD ROASTERS
163 Luckie Beans
164 Northern Edge Coffee
166 Pumphreys Coffee

NEWCASTLE

CAFE
2 Harvest
3 BLK Coffee
4 Fenwick Foodhall
5 Hatch Coffee
6 Flat Caps Coffee
7 Laneway & Co

ROASTER
10 Ouseburn Coffee Co.

MORE GOOD CUPS
114 1901 Caffe Bistro
115 Pink Lane Coffee
116 Arch Sixteen Cafe

MORE GOOD ROASTERS
165 Pink Lane Roastery

MAP 1. PILGRIMS COFFEE HOUSE

Falkland House, Marygate, Holy Island, Northumberland, TD15 2SJ

Northumberland's caffeine-hungry tourists will need to check the tide tables to ensure they don't miss out on a freshly roasted brew from Holy Island's Pilgrims Coffee House.

After a roam around the square mile isle, a visit to the historic farmhouse is a must. In warmer months you can savour a filtered single origin in the spacious walled garden, or on a chilly day cosy up with a flat white next to a roaring fire in one of the cafe's many rooms.

INSIDER'S TIP: ENERGY IS PROVIDED FROM 100 PER CENT RENEWABLE SOURCES

Owner Andrew Mundy and his "left-hand man" Jonny roast the cafe's staple blends, Daily Bread and Holy Grail, along with a myriad of single origins in the yurt out back. And you'll find freshly brewed ales like their coffee-infused best bitter, aptly named Sleep Slayer, bubbling away in one of the rooms upstairs.

The soups, sarnies and gluttonous goodies are mostly organic and all fashioned in-house with ingredients from local indies.

Sustainability is the beating heart of this family-friendly cafe. Takeaway cups are compostable and the bags, in which to haul home a bounty of beans, are biodegradable.

ESTABLISHED
2006

KEY ROASTER
Pilgrims Coffee

BREWING METHODS
Espresso,
bulk brew

MACHINES
Fiorenzato
Piazza San
Marco lever,
Kees van der
WestenMirage

GRINDERS
Mahlkonig Peak,
Anfim Super
Caimano

OPENING HOURS
Mo
9am
(wit
varia

44

Gluten FREE

BEANS AVAILABLE INSTORE

ALTERNATIVE MILK

WIFI

CYCLE FRIENDLY

OUTDOOR seating

FAMILY friendly

DISABLED ACCESS

WWW.O
Ouseburn

www.pilgrimscoffee.com T: 01289 389109
f Pilgrims Coffee House and Roastery 🐦 @pilgrimscoffee 📷 @pilgrims...

MAP№ 2. HARVEST

91 St George's Terrace, Jesmond, Newcastle upon Tyne, NE2 2DN

Harvest is the flagship store from Newcastle roasters Ouseburn Coffee Co., its cool stripped-back wood and metal counter a perfect match for the minimalistic black and white branding of OCC's coffee.

Here you'll find OCC's rich, full-bodied seasonal house espresso, alongside rotating single origins available as espresso, V60 and AeroPress. And on hot days, cold brew provides a refreshing pep up.

INSIDER'S TIP: FROM SUPPER CLUBS TO SPEAKEASY COCKTAIL NIGHTS, THERE'S NEVER A DULL MOMENT

This sleek community hub offers more than just a quality caffeine fix though. The all-day brekkie and brunch menu is a big hit with regulars: poached eggs with tasty toppings take a starring role alongside pancakes, granola and sweet and savoury pastries baked in store daily.

Come lunchtime, a crew of salads, soups and tortillas is waiting in the wings to tempt you to linger.

And if you're looking to perfect your home brewing, don't leave without a bag of seasonal coffee which the friendly baristas can match to your preference.

ESTABLISHED
2014

KEY ROASTER
Ouseburn
Coffee Co.

BREWING METHODS
Espresso, V60,
AeroPress,
cold brew

MACHINE
La Marzocco
Linea PB

GRINDER
Mahlkonig
EK 43

OPENING HOURS
Mon-Sun
8am-6pm

 Gluten FREE

 BEANS AVAILABLE INSTORE

 ALTERNATIVE MILK

 WIFI

 CYCLE FRIENDLY

 OUTDOOR seating

 FAMILY FRIENDLY

 BRING YOUR OWN cup

COFFEE COURSES

'seburncoffee.co.uk   T: 01912 707307

'offee   🐦 @ouseburncoffee   📷 @ouseburncoffee

MAP 3. BLK COFFEE

214 Chillingham Road, Heaton, Newcastle upon Tyne, NE6 5LP

Heaton's caffeine hedonists needn't splash out on pricey multi-roastery subscriptions, as the inventory of European roasters appearing on BLK's board will rival the slickest of services.

And whether you're just getting into Five Elephant, exploring new avenues via April or are already a Workshop purist, owner Alison Bell and her brigade of baristas are equipped with the latest tasting notes and serve styles to best complement your pick from the guests.

INSIDER'S TIP THERE ARE PLANS AFOOT FOR A BLK EXTENSION. WATCH THIS SPACE ...

Their super friendly approach to speciality means you'll often find the micro meeting place packed out with locals and coffee lovers taking advantage of the next-level loyalty card: five filled cards equals one bag of retail coffee, ten filled cards earns a piece of brewing equipment from the well-stocked retail shelf. #score.

And if you need a bit of guidance on your new gear, Alison also holds a range of coffee courses at the BLK lab.

ESTABLISHED
2015

KEY ROASTERS
Workshop, Square Mile, Five Elephant

BREWING METHODS
Espresso, AeroPress, Chemex, Clever Dripper, cold drip, french press, Kalita Wave, V60

MACHINE
La Marzocco Linea Classic MP

GRINDERS
Nuova Simonelli Mythos One, Mahlkonig EK 43

OPENING HOURS
Mon-Fri
7am-6pm
Sat 9am-5pm
Sun 10am-5pm

Gluten FREE

BEANS AVAILABLE INSTORE

ALTERNATIVE MILK

WIFI

CYCLE FRIENDLY

OUTDOOR seating

FAMILY friendly

COFFEE COURSES

MAP 4. FENWICK FOODHALL

39 Northumberland Street, Newcastle upon Tyne, NE1 7AS

While eating your way around Fenwick's swish food hall, don't miss the opportunity for a caffeine hit from Ouseburn Coffee Co. You'll find them in store, selling a carefully curated collection of their own-roasted coffees, which are bagged and ground to order.

Head to the hand-finished bar and the city's first indie roaster will brew you a reviving espresso. Other perfect pick-me-ups for drooping shoppers include nitro coffee and espresso martinis. Or if you're really flagging in the heat, try the fabulous cold brew created with a delicate, fruity single origin seasonal coffee that's been triple filtered and slow brewed for 20 hours.

INSIDER'S TIP RETURN COLD BREW BOTTLES FOR DISCOUNTS AND REWARDS

The emporium of edibles fuses local and international influences for an exciting multicultural food and drink experience, and the chosen coffee offering is no different. OCC beans are roasted down the road in the Ouseburn Valley and ethically sourced from speciality growers across the globe.

Roasted in small batches, the coffee is ultra fresh and sold by the gram, so you can pick up small samples of different styles to brew at home.

ESTABLISHED
2015

KEY ROASTER
Ouseburn Coffee Co.

BREWING METHODS
Espresso, nitro, cold brew

MACHINE
La Marzocco Linea PB

GRINDER
Mahlkonig EK 43

OPENING HOURS
Mon-Fri
9am-8pm
Sat 9am-7pm
Sun 11am-5pm

BEANS AVAILABLE INSTORE

ALTERNATIVE MILK

WIFI

CYCLE FRIENDLY

OUTDOOR SEATING

FAMILY FRIENDLY

DISABLED ACCESS

BRING YOUR OWN CUP

COFFEE COURSES

www.ouseburncoffee.co.uk   T: 01912 707307

f Ouseburn Coffee   🐦 @ouseburncoffee   📷 @ouseburncoffee

MAP 5. HATCH COFFEE

Ellison Place, Newcastle upon Tyne, NE1 8XS

Housed in a former parking attendant's cabin on Ellison Place, Hatch Coffee may look small from the outside, but within its walls beats the heart of a fully operational speciality coffee bar.

Head barista Mark Briston has travelled the globe to tune up his coffee skills, and it's his mission to serve *'stimulating, inspired and delightful'* coffee in every cup.

Only the best ingredients will do: seasonal espresso from Newcastle roaster Pink Lane Coffee is complemented by organic milk from Darlington's Acorn Dairy.

INSIDER'S TIP VISIT TO SEE THE CLEVER COMPACT DESIGN OF NEWCASTLE'S SMALL BUSINESS OF THE YEAR 2016

There is no shortage of tasty treats on offer to pair with your drink. Malteser tiffin or a sticky-licious caramel shortbread make for addictive pick-me-ups. There are also breakfast bars and Wolfys porridge pots to satisfy you on the go.

Extracting the most out of the compact space (the nifty design is ingenious), Hatch Coffee offers cheerful service and a great cup to-go amid the bustle of a busy community.

ESTABLISHED
2016

KEY ROASTER
Pink Lane Coffee

BREWING METHOD
Espresso

MACHINE
La Marzocco
Linea PB

GRINDERS
Mythos One,
Mazzer Mini

OPENING HOURS
Mon-Fri
7.30am-4.30pm

Gluten FREE

BEANS AVAILABLE
INSTORE

ALTERNATIVE MILK

CYCLE FRIENDLY

DISABLED ACCESS

BRING YOUR OWN Cup

---

www.hatchcoffee.com T: 07713 820905

f HatchCoffeeNewcastle 🐦 @hatchcoffee 📷 @hatchcoffeenewcastle

№6. FLAT CAPS COFFEE

9-11 Carliol Square, Newcastle upon Tyne, NE1 6UF

Photos: Chris Egon Searle

Whippets and cantankerous old men? Discard any negative associations; the flat cap is now the unofficial icon of award winning coffee.

Banker turned reigning Northern barista champ (of three years) Joe Meagher is legendary for his discipline, standards and skill.

And they're fully showcased at his Newcastle coffee shop which has moved to a new location on Carliol Square. This spacious, light and airy space has been artfully bedecked with hanging plants and festoon lighting.

Coffee insiders visit for three brew methods and a seasonal menu of beans, so there's something for every whim. And to complement the coffee alchemy, there are carefully sourced teas from London's Postcard.

INSIDER'S TIP FLAT CAPS HAS RECENTLY ORGANISED NEWCASTLE'S FIRST COFFEE FESTIVAL

Pull up a pew and watch the master at work, immersing yourself in pure theatre.

Then stay on for an exciting menu of food that includes haggis or smoked salmon brekkies, homemade smoked cheddar scones, and pork and apple sausage rolls.

ESTABLISHED
2010

KEY ROASTERS
Workshop Coffee,
Colonna Coffee,
Has Bean Coffee

BREWING METHODS
Espresso,
Kalita Wave,
AeroPress,
syphon

MACHINE
Simonelli

GRINDERS
Mahlkonig K30,
Mahlkonig EK 43,
Mahlkonig Peak

OPENING HOURS
Mon-Fri
8am-7pm
Sat 9am-6pm
Sun 9am-4pm

 Gluten FREE

 BEANS AVAILABLE INSTORE

 ALTERNATIVE MILK

WIFI

 CYCLE FRIENDLY

 FAMILY FRIENDLY

 DISABLED ACCESS

 COFFEE COURSES

www.flatcapscoffee.com   T: 01912 615748
f Flat Caps Coffee   🐦 @flatcapjoe   📷 @flatcapjoe

MAP 7. LANEWAY & CO

17-19 High Bridge, Newcastle upon Tyne, NE1 1EW

Bliss is lifting the distinctive blue rim of a Laneway & Co coffee cup to your lips and enjoying consistently good espresso crafted from the likes of London's AllPress or guest roasters Square Mile, Caravan and Origin.

And with the additional options of V60 and AeroPress, this minimalistic cafe, tucked away among the indie shops and eateries of Newcastle's cobbled High Bridge, is clearly a class act.

INSIDER'S TIP DRINK MICRO LOT FILTERS WITH TOP-NOTCH THAI CUISINE AT THE SUPPER CLUB

In summer, the alfresco bench is the one to bag, but at any time of year the floor-to-ceiling windows make it a prime spot in which to linger over an AllPress Redchurch Blend piccolo or a refreshing cold brew.

Laneway & Co has been open just one year, but the cosy coffee den is already expanding into the basement, ensuring that even more coffee lovers can get their fix of quality caffeine with fresh-from-the-oven pastries, bright salads and banging breakfasts.

Look out for the Laneway mobile stall, which keeps the hot drinks and coffee cocktails pumping at local events.

ESTABLISHED
2016

KEY ROASTER
AllPress
Espresso

BREWING METHODS
Espresso, V60,
AeroPress

MACHINE
La Marzocco
Linea PB

GRINDERS
Mazzer Robur,
Mahlkonig EK 43

OPENING HOURS
Mon-Fri
8am-6pm
Sat 9am-5pm
Sun 10am-5pm

 Gluten FREE

 BEANS AVAILABLE INSTORE

 ALTE RNA TIVE MILK

 WIFI

 FAMILY FRIENDLY

 DISABLED ACCESS

 BRING YOUR OWN Cup

www.lanewaycoffee.co.uk

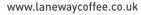

f Laneway & Co   🐦 @lanewayandco   📷 @lanewaycoffeeco

CAKESMITHS
CAKES FOR COFFEE SHOES

EST 2014
BAKED IN BRISTOL

MAP № 8. MINT HOBO

30 High Street, Yarm, Stockton on Tees, County Durham, TS15 9AE

Yarm is now well and truly on the coffee map, thanks to the crew of caffeine fiends who tailor the Mint Hobo experience to each individual who comes through the door.

Whether you're seeking a morning jolt, a fruity pick-me-up or a delicate caffeine infusion, owner Steve Ashman and team make it their mission to present you with the perfect cup. And with six single origins on the go, served as espresso or filtered through Syphon, Chemex and AeroPress, there's bound to be a bespoke coffee just for you.

INSIDER'S TIP THESE PEOPLE LIKE TO PARTY; BOOK THEM FOR YOUR NEXT KNEES UP

Attentive individualised service is the lifeblood of this welcoming cafe which prides itself on seeking out delish regional products for a menu of cakes, scones, wraps and toasties. And alongside the Rounton Coffee (roasted in nearby East Rounton) there's a chance to quaff local beers, smoothies and speciality hot chocolate.

'The welcome, water and bathroom are always free,' smiles Steve, who aims to make Mint Hobo a home from home on the high street and regularly packs in coffeeholics at tasting events. 'We love our customers more than coffee – and that's a lot.'

ESTABLISHED
2015

KEY ROASTER
Rounton Coffee Roasters

BREWING METHODS
Espresso, Syphon, Chemex, AeroPress

MACHINE
Sanremo Opera

GRINDER
Mahlkonig EK 43

OPENING HOURS
Mon-Thu
7am-7pm
Fri 7am-10pm
Sat 7am-7pm
Sun 9am-5pm

Gluten FREE

BEANS AVAILABLE INSTORE

ALTERNATIVE MILK

WIFI

CYCLE FRIENDLY

OUTDOOR SEATING

FAMILY FRIENDLY

COFFEE COURSES

---

www.minthobo.co.uk   T: 07763 895806
f Mint Hobo   🐦 @minthobo   📷 @minthobo

ROASTERS

MAP №9. PILGRIMS COFFEE

Falkland House, Marygate, Holy Island, Northumberland, TD15 2SJ

Roasting beans in a yurt on the Northumberland island of Lindisfarne, Andrew Mundy may have one of the best jobs in coffee.

He mans the helm of Pilgrims Coffee, roasting speciality grade beans in small batches, using Cropster software and a modified gas drum roaster.

'It's all about care and respect' asserts Andrew, which extends to responsibility for the stunning natural environment surrounding the roastery.

The business is built on sustainability; it uses 100 per cent renewable energy in the cafe, ethically sources its beans and uses biodegradable bags and compostable labels. It's also recently added a second skin to the roaster drum for cleaner tasting coffee.

'TIME THE TIDES RIGHT TO JOIN ONE OF THE ROASTERY TOURS'

Buying beans from across the world via importer Falcon, the family-run company is also currently setting up direct trade with a small shade-grown coffee farm in India.

'We just really like coffee,' smiles Andrew, and it's plain to see. Time the tides right, and you may be able to join one of the roastery tours. Just avoid hot days, as roaster Jonny has been known to don *'dangerously meagre denim shorts'* when it gets warm in the yurt. You've been warned!

ESTABLISHED
2013

ROASTER
MAKE & SIZE
Ozturk modified
gas drum
10kg

CAFE ONSITE

OPEN TO THE PUBLIC

BEANS AVAILABLE
ONSITE
ONLINE

---

www.pilgrimscoffee.com   T: 01289 389109
f Pilgrims Coffee House and Roastery   🐦 @pilgrimscoffee   📷 @pilgrimscoffeehouse

MAP 10. OUSEBURN COFFEE CO.

Unit 25, Albion Row, Newcastle upon Tyne, NE6 1LQ

As Newcastle's first established indie roaster, Ouseburn Coffee Co. continues to pioneer great coffee through ethically sourced, speciality beans which are roasted and bagged the same day in the heart of the Ouseburn Valley.

It's here that the flagship espresso blend and a clutch of speciality coffees are roasted daily, alongside regular micro lots and bi-monthly seasonal specials which reflect the global coffee harvests.

This dedicated crew started selling coffee at local markets (which they still do) and opened their thriving cafe, Harvest in Jesmond, in the summer of 2014, further expanding operations to the city centre last year inside the newly refurbished Fenwick Foodhall.

STAY TUNED ON SOCIAL MEDIA TO FOLLOW THE BURSTING CALENDAR OF EVENTS AND SPECIALITY FOOD MARKETS

Since 2012, these small bags of coffee thrills have been a big hit with trade and home brew fans alike. The roastery is currently available to visit by appointment only, though you can buy fresh beans, enjoy a brew and meet the guys at the markets in Tynemouth Station and Newcastle Quayside every weekend as well as at regular monthly food events across the region.

ESTABLISHED
2012

ROASTER
MAKE & SIZE
Toper Cafemino
5kg

OPEN
BY APPOINTMENT

COFFEE
COURSES

BEANS
AVAILABLE

ONLINE

www.ouseburncoffee.co.uk   T: 01912 307307

f Ouseburn Coffee Co   🐦 @ouseburncoffee   📷 @ouseburncoffee

ᴺ⁰·11. TYNEMOUTH COFFEE COMPANY

Unit 4, Back Stormont Street, North Shields, Tyne and Wear, NE29 0EY

Speciality coffee shops, delis, restaurants and offices across the UK eagerly anticipate the arrival of their Tynemouth Coffee Company delivery. That's because they're confident that each bag of beans will be ultra fresh, having been meticulously hand roasted the previous day.

With six delightfully named blends to choose from they can be assured that something will hit the sweet spot for their customers and employees.

CALL IF YOU'RE LOOKING FOR ADVICE ON EQUIPMENT FOR YOUR NEW VENTURE OR WANT TO UPGRADE

That could be the caffeine jolt of a single origin Colombian in Rocket Fuel, the brilliant bean blend with Colombian and Brazilian beans in the Bobby Dazzler or the caffeinated Colombian day-starter, Jingling Geordie.

Ethics are high on the agenda at this artisan roastery with the crew on a mission to source, roast and brew the best quality coffee and to educate customers. The team are also firm advocates for using quality equipment, so stock a range of traditional espresso and bean-to-cup machines to suit every budget. And to help everyone get the best from their beans, there are barista and home brew courses too.

ESTABLISHED
2009

ROASTER
MAKE & SIZE
Toper
12kg

OPEN
BY APPOINTMENT

COFFEE
COURSES

BEANS
AVAILABLE

ONSITE

ONLINE

---

www.tynemouthcoffee.com   T: 01912 600995

f Tynemouth Coffee Company   🐦 @tynemouthcoffee   📷 @tynemouth_coffee

CUMBRIA, LANCASHIRE, MERSEYSIDE & NORTH WALES

> KING STREET COFFEE COMPANY №31

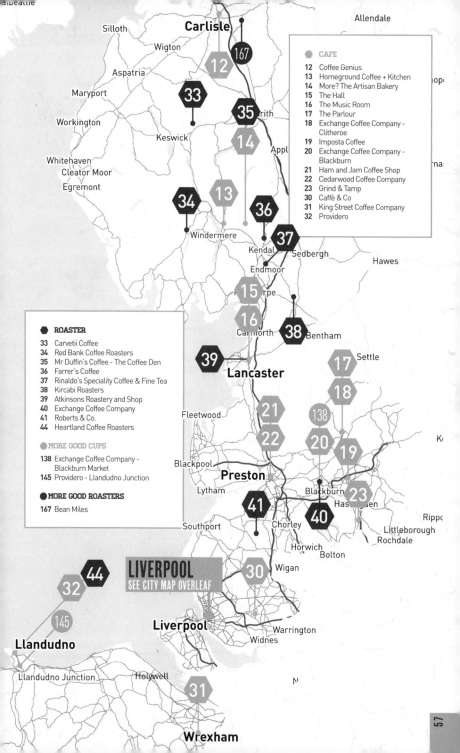

CAFE

12 Coffee Genius
13 Homeground Coffee + Kitchen
14 More? The Artisan Bakery
15 The Hall
16 The Music Room
17 The Parlour
18 Exchange Coffee Company - Clitheroe
19 Imposta Coffee
20 Exchange Coffee Company - Blackburn
21 Ham and Jam Coffee Shop
22 Cedarwood Coffee Company
23 Grind & Tamp
30 Caffè & Co
31 King Street Coffee Company
32 Providero

ROASTER

33 Carvetii Coffee
34 Red Bank Coffee Roasters
35 Mr Duffin's Coffee - The Coffee Den
36 Farrer's Coffee
37 Rinaldo's Speciality Coffee & Fine Tea
38 Kircabi Roasters
39 Atkinsons Roastery and Shop
40 Exchange Coffee Company
41 Roberts & Co.
44 Heartland Coffee Roasters

MORE GOOD CUPS

138 Exchange Coffee Company - Blackburn Market
145 Providero - Llandudno Junction

MORE GOOD ROASTERS

167 Bean Miles

LIVERPOOL
SEE CITY MAP OVERLEAF

LIVERPOOL

CAFE

24 Roast Coffee & Kitchen
25 Root Coffee
26 Bold Street Coffee
27 92 Degrees Coffee
28 Community SOUL
29 In Spire Coffee Bar

ROASTER

42 Crosby Coffee
43 Neighbourhood Coffee

MORE GOOD CUPS

139 Panna Kitchen & Canteen
140 Filter + Fox
141 Coffee & Fandisha
142 Blooming Skull Coffee

MORE GOOD ROASTERS

177 92 Degrees Coffee

MAP №12. COFFEE GENIUS

20 St Cuthbert's Lane, Carlisle, Cumbria, CA3 8AG

Since opening in March 2014, the relaxed surroundings of Coffee Genius in Carlisle have provided Cumbria's caffeine obsessives with an oasis of quality and choice.

Having recently added cold brew to its repertoire, there are now seven brew methods available, making it the only place in the city to offer such variety. On the bean front, three single origins are to be found at any time alongside the house blend from Carvetii.

INSIDER'S TIP FANCY A LITTLE EXTRA KICK? CHECK OUT THE SECRET ESPRESSO COCKTAIL MENU

Lynn and Mike Steadman's cafe has attracted popular acclaim: *Carlisle Living* has crowned it Best Cafe twice, and with its team of passionate baristas handling an ever-changing selection of coffees with great care, it's easy to understand why.

There is more to Coffee Genius than just caffeine though; it's also loved for its sweet selection of homemade cakes, scones and croissants served warm from the oven.

An expanding gluten-free and dairy-free menu (try the vegan millionaire's cake) means everyone can get in on the edible action. There are after-hours antics too, with jazz and cocktail nights on the agenda for 2017.

ESTABLISHED
2014

KEY ROASTER
Carvetii
Coffee Roasters

BREWING METHODS
Espresso,
Chemex,
AeroPress,
V60, cafetiere,
syphon,
cold brew

MACHINE
La Marzocco

GRINDERS
Mahlkonig K30,
Mahlkonig
Tanzania,
Mazzer Mini

OPENING HOURS
Mon-Sat
8.30am-5pm
Sun
10.30am-4pm

 Gluten FREE

 BEANS AVAILABLE INSTORE

 ALTERNATIVE MILK

 WIFI

 OUTDOOR seating

 FAMILY FRIENDLY

 DISABLED ACCESS

BRING YOUR OWN Cup.

www.coffeegenius.co.uk   T: 01228 546594

f Coffee Genius   🐦 @coffeegenius1   📷 @coffeegenius1

№13. HOMEGROUND COFFEE + KITCHEN

Main Road, Windermere, Cumbria, LA23 1DX

There are lots of cafes vying for visitors' attention in touristy Windermere, but Homeground is one worth hunting out if you're serious about high quality coffee – and also want to stuff your face.

It's usually deluged with customers sitting out front, feasting on the all-day brunch and slurping Carvetii coffee. The espresso is excellent and complemented by batch brew and V60 from a rotating group of roasters, in which Atkinsons often features.

INSIDER'S TIP TRY THE 'SECRET RECIPE' HASH BROWNS

The food at Homeground is seriously good and includes thrills such as a sizzling skillet of baked tandoori cauliflower with yogurt, spinach and tomatoes, topped with a foot-long piece of garlicky flat bread, lightly charred and perfect for scooping. Warning: licking buttery fingers is non-negotiable.

Owners Richard and Jane have created a hub in the community, injecting creativity and implementing the highest standards in all areas. Visit to enjoy homebaked cakes, decent veggie and vegan options, local Hawkeshead ales and the friendly vibe.

ESTABLISHED
2015

KEY ROASTERS
Carvetii Coffee Roasters, Atkinsons

BREWING METHODS
Espresso, V60, batch brew

MACHINE
La Marzocco Custom Linea PB

GRINDERS
Mahlkonig Peak, Nuova Simonelli Mythos One, Mahlkonig EK 43

OPENING HOURS
Mon-Sun
9am-5pm

www.homegroundcafe.co.uk T: 01539 444863
f Homeground Coffee + Kitchen 🐦 @homegroundcafe 📷 @homegroundcafe

14. MORE? THE ARTISAN BAKERY

Middle of Mill Yard, Staveley, near Kendal, Cumbria, LA8 9LR

Situated at Stavely Mill Yard, More? is the natural habitat for coffee-loving adventurers exploring the Lake District.

Cyclists, walkers and tourists are drawn to the bakery to snaffle rabbit and fennel sausage rolls and hand-raised pork pies with piccalilli, along with coffee to-go from Red Bank Roasters.

INSIDER'S TIP SWING BY EARLY FOR A HOMEMADE SOURDOUGH CROISSANT

And while hungry visitors might want to take on the challenge of the Full Shabba burger with cheese, roast onion and chilli jam, others plump for lightly toasted walnut and raisin bread or the enormous meringues.

And anyone would swoon over the slabs of traybake (More? holds 39 Great Taste Awards for their bakery products), creamy flat whites and filter from the batch brewer.

Don't leave without a loaf of Patrick's famously satisfying sourdough: beautiful to look at, sensual to hold, enticing to smell and delicious to devour.

ESTABLISHED
2006

KEY ROASTER
Ozone Coffee Roasters

BREWING METHODS
Espresso, V60, ICB batch brew

MACHINE
La Marzocco Linea PB

GRINDERS
Nuova Simonelli Mythos One, Mahlkonig EK 43

OPENING HOURS
Mon-Fri
7.30am-5pm
Sat-Sun
7.30am-5.30pm

Gluten FREE

BEANS AVAILABLE INSTORE

WIFI

CYCLE FRIENDLY

OUTDOOR seating

www.moreartisan.co.uk T: 01539 822297

f More? The Artisan Bakery 🐦 @moreartisan 📷 @more_bakery

MAP 15. THE HALL

10 China Street, Lancaster, Lancashire, LA1 1EX

Atkinsons roastery HQ enjoys the prestigious setting of Lancaster's old parish hall, which it has transformed into a contemporary, canteen-style cafe.

Peeling back the layers of history during the building works, Ian Steel and crew discovered a sprung maple dance floor, and by introducing a grand piano for live music and DJ decks for vinyl nights, The Hall has once more become a centre of hip happenings.

By day you'll find it packed with the city's cofferati, who visit to appreciate the exceptional coffee crafted from beans toasted to perfection in the adjoining roastery. If you ask nicely, Ian is happy to give customers a whistlestop tour of the roastery including its vintage Whitmees and new, state-of-the-art, stainless steel Loring roaster.

INSIDER'S TIP LOOK OUT FOR ATKINSONS IN THE NORTHERN QUARTER FOOD HALL AT MACKIE MAYOR

With a bakery on site – don't miss the delightful Debbie's Guinness gingerbread cake with fresh peach – and the exotic bean shop next door, this is the original must-visit for brew fans, bean freaks and the caffeine curious.

ESTABLISHED
2013

KEY ROASTER
Atkinsons

BREWING METHODS
Espresso, Chemex, nitro, batch brew, cold brew, syphon

MACHINES
La Marzocco Strada EP, 1959 Faema President

GRINDERS
Nuova Simonelli Mythos One, Mazzer Robur, Mahlkonig EK 43

OPENING HOURS
Mon-Thu 8am-6pm
Fri-Sat 8am-10pm
Sun 10am-5pm

Gluten FREE

BEANS AVAILABLE INSTORE

ALTERNATIVE MILK

WIFI

CYCLE FRIENDLY

FAMILY FRIENDLY

DISABLED ACCESS

BRING YOUR OWN Cup

COFFEE COURSES

www.thecoffeehopper.com T: 01524 65470

f Priory Hall 🐦 @coffeehopper 📷 @atkinsons.coffee

MAP 16. THE MUSIC ROOM

Sun Square, Lancaster, Lancashire, LA1 1EW

Probably the most beautiful building in this year's coffee guide, The Music Room calls a 1730s rococo pavilion home. The heritage space was re-imagined as a contemporary speciality coffee shop by brew brothers Maitland and Caspar Steel in what turned out to be the first in a collection of Atkinsons coffee experiences.

To visit, brew hunters must first find the tiny Georgian passageway that leads from a busy shopping street to Sun Square. And there, on outdoor seating strewn with fleeces and rugs, they'll stumble upon a band of speciality coffee fans who are already in the know.

INSIDER'S TIP EXPECT ARTWORK INSIDE AND OUT AS THE COFFEE QUARTER BECOMES THE CULTURAL QUARTER

Inside, clean lined modernism reigns, with laptop warriors on the mezzanine level fuelled by homemade cakes from the house bakery, sipping coffee brewed from own-roasted beans.

Cold brew and a mean pourover are the house specialities which are, as owner Ian Steel asserts, *'perfect for those looking for a brighter style of coffee – in the sun'*.

ESTABLISHED
2011

KEY ROASTER
Atkinsons

BREWING METHODS
Espresso, V60, AeroPress, batch brew, cold brew

MACHINE
Sanremo Cafe Racer

GRINDERS
Nuova Simonelli Mythos, Mahlkonig EK 43

OPENING HOURS
Mon-Sat
10am-5pm
Sun
11am-4pm

 Gluten FREE

 BEANS AVAILABLE INSTORE

 ALTERNATIVE MILK

 WIFI

 CYCLE FRIENDLY

 OUTDOOR Seating

 DISABLED ACCESS

 BRING YOUR OWN Cup

 COFFEE COURSES

www.thecoffeehopper.com T: 01524 65470

f The Music Room 🐦 @coffeehopper 📷 @musicroomcafe

MAP 17. THE PARLOUR

19-21 Wellgate, Clitheroe, Lancashire, BB7 2DP

MY MUM DOESNT LIKE YOU & SHE LIKES EVERY RUM

Don't even think about ordering a caramel latte, decaf cappuccino or loose-leaf infusion, as only hardcore caffeine and hard booze breaches the bar at Clitheroe's new hangout.

Dealing in '50% cocktails, 40% caffeine and 10% sarcasm', The Parlour isn't your average coffee shop, but serving expertly crafted Heart and Graft espresso alongside a killer collection of curious concoctions, the industrial space is a definite go-to for post-work bevvies and weekend thrills.

INSIDER'S TIP STOCK UP ON BEANS BEFORE YOU LEAVE; YOUR HANGOVER WILL THANK YOU TOMORROW

Alongside beans from the Salford roastery and hard liquor is a collection of freak-shake specials – Kinder Bueno anyone? – and a small collection of cookies.

Yet what The Parlour lacks in savoury sustenance it makes up for in badass tunes, Instagram opportunities and (optional) banter from the band of baristas and mixologists behind the bar.

ESTABLISHED
2016

KEY ROASTER
Heart and Graft Coffee Roasters

BREWING METHOD
Espresso

MACHINES
Faema E61, Faema President

GRINDER
Mazzer

OPENING HOURS
Tue-Wed
10am-5pm
Thu 10am-10pm
Fri 10am-12.30am
Sat 10am-11.30pm

BEANS AVAILABLE
INSTORE

WIFI

CYCLE FRIENDLY

www.theparlourclitheroe.com T: 01200 425666

f The Parlour   @theparlourclitheroe

ₙₒ18. EXCHANGE COFFEE COMPANY

24 Wellgate, Clitheroe, Lancashire, BB7 2DP

Wander down Wellgate and you can't avoid being enveloped in the exquisite scent of fresh coffee wafting from Exchange.

'Fresh' really is the word, as you'll discover if you follow your nose to this delightful Victorian coffee house.

With beans roasted on site, the crew at Exchange practise what they preach when they claim that *'the secret of great coffee is its freshness'*. Watch the roasting in action while browsing a choice of over 35 varieties of single origin and blended coffees.

INSIDER'S TIP CLIMB TO THE THIRD FLOOR TO FIND A PEACEFUL SPOT IN WHICH TO SIP YOUR BREW

And once you've chosen from espresso, cafetiere or drip, cosy up on an antique armchair in front of the fire to soak up the nostalgia: William Morris wallpaper and antiques come as standard here.

The TARDIS-like building is spread over three floors, serving delicious sarnies, jacket potatoes and cakes throughout the day, and houses a shop that's packed full of all the coffee gear your heart could desire.

ESTABLISHED
1992

KEY ROASTER
Exchange Coffee Company

BREWING METHODS
Espresso, french press, Clever Dripper

MACHINE
La Marzocco GB5

GRINDERS
Mahlkonig K30, Mignon, Ditting KR804

OPENING HOURS
Mon-Sat
9am-5.30pm (coffee house closes at 5pm)

 Gluten FREE

 BEANS AVAILABLE INSTORE

 ALTERNATIVE MILK

 WIFI

 CYCLE FRIENDLY

 OUTDOOR seating

 FAMILY FRIENDLY

 DISABLED ACCESS

 BRING YOUR OWN Cup.

 COFFEE COURSES ◄

www.exchangecoffee.co.uk   T: 01200 442270

f Exchange Coffee Company   🐦 @exchange_coffee   📷 @exchange_coffee

MAP 19. IMPOSTA COFFEE

1 Abbey Street, Accrington, Lancashire, BB5 1EN

Happy in the knowledge that you're going to be sinking a decent cup – courtesy of Coopers Coffee's award winning Louie Mio blend – the only difficult decision you'll face at Imposta Coffee is choosing which edibles to accompany it with.

And once you've weighed up the merits of the homemade pastel de nata versus gooey chocolate brownies or freshly-baked fruit scones (all made by owner Paul's mum at her B&B kitchen), settle in and enjoy the goodies in comfortable and cosy surroundings with the day's newspapers.

INSIDER'S TIP CHECK OUT IMPOSTA'S FACEBOOK PAGE FOR COFFEE COMPS AND OFFERS

With its prime position on the corner of Abbey Street and Avenue Parade in Accrington's town centre, this popular coffee shop makes a good lunch stop for its pleasing range of hot sandwiches on ciabatta – the topside of beef with swiss cheese, red onion and chutney is a killer combo loved by locals.

Need a commuter's caffeine fix? Grab a coffee to-go – it's open bright and early from 8am.

ESTABLISHED
2010

KEY ROASTER
Coopers Coffee

BREWING METHOD
Espresso

MACHINE
Astoria

GRINDERS
Dalla Corte
grind on
demand x 2

OPENING HOURS
Mon-Sat
8am-3pm

Gluten FREE

BEANS AVAILABLE INSTORE

ALTERNATIVE MILK

WIFI

CYCLE FRIENDLY

OUTDOOR seating

FAMILY friendly

DISABLED ACCESS

BRING YOUR OWN Cup

COFFEE COURSES

www.impostacoffee.co.uk　T: 01254 351333

f Imposta Coffee　@ @impostacoffee

20. EXCHANGE COFFEE COMPANY

13-15 Fleming Square, Blackburn, Lancashire, BB2 2DG

Meander past the cathedral and make your way over the road to Fleming Square where you'll find Exchange Coffee's original roasting shop in one of the oldest parts of Blackburn.

A team of roasters work from this historic building and visitors are greeted with the sweet waft of freshly roasted beans as they cross the threshold of the impressive stone arch frontage.

INSIDER'S TIP THE GUYS HAVE A COFFEE BAR IN BLACKBURN MARKET TOO

Once the collection of over 35 artisan coffees and range of brewing methods have been considered, find a pew downstairs in the airy first floor seating area or grab a table in the square outside and indulge in a spot of people watching.

The top-notch caffeine experience is enhanced by a menu of sandwiches, toasties and homemade specials – not forgetting some enticing cakes.

As a newly-inducted Exchange evangelist (trust us, you will be), invite all your friends and head next door, where you can luxuriate in oak-panelled splendour in the 1849 private dining room, which seats 8–20.

ESTABLISHED
1986

KEY ROASTER
Exchange Coffee Company

BREWING METHODS
Espresso, Clever Dripper, french press

MACHINE
Cimbali M34

GRINDERS
Mahlkonig K30, Ditting KR804, Mignon

OPENING HOURS
Mon-Sat
9am-5.30pm (coffee house closes 5pm)

 Gluten FREE

 BEANS AVAILABLE INSTORE

 ALTERNATIVE MILK

 WIFI

 CYCLE FRIENDLY

 OUTDOOR seating

 FAMILY FRIENDLY

 DISABLED ACCESS

 BRING YOUR OWN Cup

 COFFEE COURSES

---

www.exchangecoffee.co.uk   T: 01254 54258

f Exchange Coffee Company   🐦 @exchange_coffee   📷 @exchange_coffee

MANCHESTER
COFFEE
FESTIVAL

4-5/11/17
VICTORIA WAREHOUSE
MANCHESTER

TALKS
CINEMA
TASTING
BREWING
ROASTERS
WORKSHOPS
COMPETITION

@CUPNORTH

Tickets at CUPNORTH.CO.UK

BROUGHT TO YOU BY:

MAP 21. HAM AND JAM COFFEE SHOP

50-52 Lancaster Road, Preston, Lancashire, PR1 1DD

Introducing speciality coffee to Preston's cultural quarter in 2015, Ham and Jam is not just a contemporary coffee shop; it's the polestar for creativity in the city.

'We started featuring work from up-and-coming local artists as we didn't have any money to spend decorating the cafe,' explains owner Richard Lowthian. *'However, it turned out that hosting regularly changing exhibitions enables us to introduce quality coffee to a whole new audience each month.'*

INSIDER'S TIP POP-UP RESTAURANT NIGHTS ARE IN THE PIPELINE

Lancaster roaster Atkinsons' Archetype and Prototype blends fuel all manner of inventive events at the cafe, from the free meditation classes to regular storytelling groups and poetry slams.

And produce from Preston's nearby covered market feeds Ham and Jam's homemade foodie haul. Skip toast at home and visit for a bonza brekkie of local sausages and bacon topped with a free range egg, followed by a wedge of carrot and pecan cake.

ESTABLISHED
2015

KEY ROASTER
Atkinsons

BREWING METHODS
Espresso, filter

MACHINE
Sanremo Zoe

GRINDER
Sanremo

OPENING HOURS
Mon-Sat
8.30am-5.30pm
Sun
10am-4.30pm

Gluten FREE

ALTE RNA TIVE MILK

WIFI

CYCLE FRIENDLY

FAMILY FRIENDLY

DISABLED ACCESS

www.hamandjamcoffeeshop.com T: 01772 827430

f Ham and Jam Coffee Shop 🐦 @hamandjampr1 📷 @ham_and_jam_preston

MAP №22. CEDARWOOD COFFEE COMPANY

10 Winckley Street, Preston, Lancashire, PR1 2AA

This sleek little set-up on Winckley Street may appear small on first impression, but pass the bar and venture upstairs to discover plenty of space in which to chair your next caffeine fuelled catch-up.

The tall stools at the ground floor window bar are perfect for watching busy shoppers scuttle along the cobbles below, or chatting with the baristas about the latest coffee tasting notes.

INSIDER'S TIP ASK NICELY AND YOU MAY GET A SHOT OF ESPRESSO IN YOUR SHAKE

Local roasters Atkinsons and Red Bank tussle for your attention in the hoppers, both offering knockout beans to be enjoyed with milk as espresso or as your pick from the filter fraternity.

Edible options are kept simple, though the small collection of toasted sandwiches and panini will certainly keep you going. Plus you'll want to save room for a couple of scoops of Bonds and Wallings ice cream from the counter – the caramel affogato is a knockout.

A cluster of tables outside, extended opening hours in summer and a killer craft beer list makes Cedarwood both your pre- and post-work saviour.

ESTABLISHED
2015

KEY ROASTER
Atkinsons

BREWING METHODS
Espresso, V60, AeroPress, cafetiere

MACHINE
Sanremo Verona

GRINDER
Sanremo

OPENING HOURS
Mon-Fri
9am-5pm
Sat-Sun
10am-5pm

BEANS AVAILABLE
INSTORE

ALTERNATIVE MILK

WIFI

OUTDOOR SEATING

www.cedarwood.coffee T: 01772 821769

f Cedarwood Coffee 🐦 @winckleystreet 📷 @cedarwoodcoffeeco

MAP № 23. GRIND & TAMP

45 Bridge Street, Ramsbottom, Bury, Lancashire, BL0 9AD

With a five-strong bill of beans, an arsenal of filter kit and regular cupping sessions, Adrian didn't water down his speciality standards when he introduced artisan coffee to Ramsbottom.

An illustrated brew bar festoons the floor-to-ceiling window of this charming old brick building, enticing Lancashire locals and coffee-minded tourists to the caffeinated embrace of Grind & Tamp.

INSIDER'S TIP BRUSH UP ON YOUR BREW SKILLS WITH A HOME BARISTA COURSE

On hand to guide novices through the house coffee and guest roasters is a troop of chummy baristas, well versed in the tasting notes.

Those already advancing to intermediate level will enjoy exploring three hand-brewed single origin options and revelling in the fruity flavours of 24-hour cold brew.

Naturally, the same level of care and quality goes into the kitchen's output. If you're stopping for a fix first thing, fuel up at the porridge bar or sample the sausage, egg and cheese toasted English muffins. Come lunch, there's the signature grilled cheese, salad of the week and hot soup to get stuck into.

ESTABLISHED
2016

KEY ROASTERS
Atkinsons, North Star Coffee Roasters, Heart and Graft Coffee Roasters

BREWING METHODS
Espresso, V60, Chemex, AeroPress, syphon

MACHINE
Sanremo Verona RS

GRINDERS
Mythos One Clima Pro, Mahlkonig K30, Mazzer

OPENING HOURS
Mon-Tue
8.30am-4pm
Thu-Sat
8.30am-4pm
Sun 10am-4pm

Gluten FREE

BEANS AVAILABLE INSTORE

ALTERNATIVE MILK

WIFI

CYCLE FRIENDLY

FAMILY FRIENDLY

BRING YOUR OWN CUP

COFFEE COURSES

---

www.grindandtampcoffee.uk   T: 01706 558030

f Grind & Tamp   🐦 @grind_tamp   📷 @grind_tamp

№24. ROAST COFFEE & KITCHEN

33 Crosby Road North, Waterloo, Liverpool, Merseyside, L22 4QB

Flat-toting hipsters, busy mums with buggies and chipper OAPs throng under one colourful roof for Roast Coffee & Kitchen's brimming brunch plates, dirty burgers and cracking cappuccinos.

Practically everything used in the kitchen is sourced within 10 miles of this busy social hub, so whether you're tucking into rustic salt beef hash, a NYC-style meatball sub or going all out with a bananaberry pancake stack, you're also feeding the local community.

INSIDER'S TIP STOCK UP ON BEANS FROM LOCAL ROASTER CROSBY AT THE COUNTER

This indie ethos extends to the caffeine offering, which is supplied by down-the-road-roasters Crosby Coffee. There's a house blend to sample as espresso with milk – earthy tones with a nutty finish – and an additional northern guest roast available as cafetiere.

A crammed calendar of events sees everything from supper clubs and cupping events to art nights and live music evenings at this spacious cafe. And the monthly burger kitchen – we're talking sky-high patties, filthy sides and wicked shakes – is a greedy highlight to indulge in throughout the year.

ESTABLISHED
2015

KEY ROASTER
Crosby Coffee

BREWING METHODS
Espresso,
cafetiere

MACHINE
Expobar G10

GRINDER
Casadio Enea
On Demand

OPENING HOURS
Mon-Fri
8am-4pm
Sat 9am-4pm
Sun 10am-3pm

 Gluten FREE

 BEANS AVAILABLE INSTORE

 ALTERNATIVE MILK

WIFI

 FAMILY FRIENDLY

 DISABLED & ACCESS

www.roastcoffeeandkitchen.com T: 01515 381820

f Roast Coffee & Kitchen   🐦 @roastcoffeeshop   📷 @roast_coffeeandkitchen

№25. ROOT COFFEE

52 Hanover Street, Liverpool, Merseyside, L1 4AF

While coffee culture newbies may blanch at the graphs and tremble at terms such as 'varietal' on the board at this city centre coffee shop, when it comes to speciality spiel, they're a blagger's best friend.

With a regularly changing espresso alongside a roster of European roasters in the filter guest spot, the handy board covers all the bases, from cup size and brewing options to bean origin and flavour notes.

A clan of clued-up baristas are also on hand with advice on roasting characteristics and flavour profiles, as well as thoughts on which bean you should choose for your flat white.

INSIDER'S TIP — ROOT IS TAKING PART IN A BARISTA EXCHANGE WITH A SPECIALITY SHOP IN BEIJING

On the food front, Root's kitchen credentials have been kicked up a couple of notches this year with the appointment of a former Michelin starred head chef.

Don't sweat that you'll be forking out big time for this gourmet grub however; plates such as ox cheek pancetta with sweet potato puree come in at under a tenner.

ESTABLISHED
2015

KEY ROASTERS
Round Hill Roastery, Craft House Coffee

BREWING METHODS
Espresso, V60, AeroPress, Chemex

MACHINE
Black Eagle Gravitech

GRINDERS
Mythos One, Mahlkonig EK 43, Mahlkonig Peak

OPENING HOURS
Mon-Sat
8.30am-6.30pm
Sat 9am-6pm
Sun 9am-6pm

 BEANS AVAILABLE INSTORE

 ALTERNATIVE MILK

 WIFI

 CYCLE FRIENDLY

 OUTDOOR seating

 FAMILY friendly

 DISABLED ACCESS

 BRING YOUR OWN cup.

www.rootcoffee.co.uk

f Root Coffee   🐦 @rootcoffeeliv   📷 @rootcoffeeliv

MAP № 26. BOLD STREET COFFEE

89 Bold Street, Liverpool, L1 4HF

An early pioneer of the speciality coffee scene in the North, Bold Street has led the pack in Liverpool since 2010, thrilling its loyal band of regulars with a winning mix of top-notch coffee and incredible edibles.

Serious about great coffee while still being lighthearted in its approach, you'll find customers grooving to the collection of classic vinyl while sipping espresso based coffees crafted from the Has Bean house roast. Guests on filter from Square Mile, Workshop, The Barn and Round Hill change weekly.

INSIDER'S TIP LOOK OUT FOR NEW VEGGIE AND VEGAN MENU OPTIONS

Having taken the Best Cafe gong in the Liverpool Food and Drink Awards three times, it's no surprise to find lovely grub to accompany the brew.

Breakfasts are a big deal here with homemade everything. Creative dishes such as Venezuelan eggs with avocado, chilli and freshly grated Venezuelan chocolate will start your day with Latin zip, especially when accompanied by South American beans on filter.

ESTABLISHED
2010

KEY ROASTER
Has Bean Coffee

BREWING METHODS
Espresso, Chemex, AeroPress

MACHINE
La Marzocco Linea PB

GRINDERS
Mythos, Mahlkonig EK 43, Anfim

OPENING HOURS
Mon-Fri
7.30am-6pm
Sat 8am-6pm
Sun 9.30am-5pm

www.boldstreetcoffee.co.uk T: 01517 070760

f Bold Street Coffee   🐦 @boldstcoffee   📷 @boldstreetcoffee

27. 92 DEGREES COFFEE

24 Hardman Street, Liverpool, Merseyside, L1 9AX

Keen-nosed coffee enthusiasts shouldn't have any trouble finding this cafe, micro roastery and former police station, as the sweet caramel notes of the freshly roasted Hope Street espresso blend extend a siren-like call to passersby.

Once inside, reward your senses with an expertly pulled espresso and a slice of banana, chocolate and hazelnut loaf at one of the communal tables or sink into a Chesterfield sofa and enjoy the sights and sounds of the working roastery.

INSIDER'S TIP TRY THE CONNOISSEUR DECAF: FRESHLY ROASTED, FRESHLY GROUND, SWISS WATER PROCESS

92 Degrees' in-house roastery supplies the cafe (and a legion of online followers) with up to four single origins – best sampled as filters at the bar – and two house espresso blends: one chocolatey, the other sharp and fruity. You'll also find small batch cold brew on the menu.

There's plenty of space to spread out and work, admire the collection of local artwork or simply savour a brew. And locally stuffed sarnies, wraps and flat breads are available at the bar until the students, office workers and tourists run the stocks down to nothing.

ESTABLISHED
2015

KEY ROASTER
92 Degrees
Coffee

BREWING METHODS
Espresso, V60,
cold brew

MACHINES
Expobar Diamant,
Marco Ecoboiler

GRINDERS
Mazzer Robur,
Mazzer Mini x 2,
Eureka Drogheria,
Mahlkonig
Tanzania

OPENING HOURS
Mon-Fri
7.45am-7pm
Sat 10am-7pm
Sun 10am-6pm

www.92degreescoffee.com   T:01517 091145

f 92DegreesCoffee   🐦 @92degreescoffee   📷 @92degreescoffee

MAP № 28. COMMUNITY SOUL

117 Wallasey Village, Wallasey, Merseyside, CH45 3LF

Amid a busy schedule of craft clubs, knit-and-natters, open mic nights and sociable suppers, the team of volunteers behind this community cafe also find time to craft seriously good coffee.

And between scrabble matches and creative workshops, the SCA-standard baristas (trained to speciality standard in-house) serve Bradford-based Limini Coffee, alongside a menu of hearty homemade soups, filled croissants and scones smothered in Cornish clotted cream and strawberry jam.

INSIDER'S TIP THE ICE CREAM SHACK IN THE GARDEN WAS BUILT BY LOCAL YOUNGSTERS

In summer Community SOUL's spoils are best enjoyed in the urban alleyway garden, where wheelie bins and weeds have been replaced with upcyled furniture and potted plants.

A Christian-centred mission to connect the community through quality coffee and good food is demonstrated through regular Soul Suppers at the cosy cafe for those living alone, along with a wealth of community projects.

ESTABLISHED
2013

KEY ROASTER
Limini Coffee

BREWING METHODS
Espresso, filter

MACHINE
La Spaziale
S9 Compact

GRINDER
La Spaziale
12 grind on
Demand

OPENING HOURS
Tue-Sat
10am-4.30pm

 Gluten FREE

 BEANS AVAILABLE INSTORE

 ALTERNATIVE MILK

 WIFI

 OUTDOOR seating

 FAMILY Friendly

 DISABLED ACCESS

 COFFEE COURSES

T: 01513 457164
f Community SOUL 🐦 @commsoul 📷 @communitysoulcoffee

№29. IN SPIRE COFFEE BAR

Aspiration Trust, The Spire, Breck Road, Wallasey, Merseyside, CH44 3BD

Community spirit must be at an all-time high in Wallasey, as this social enterprise and volunteer-led cafe is the second to open in the Merseyside town.

Occupying the basement of a formerly derelict church, In Spire trains budding baristas in the coffee shop basics and helps tackle unemployment, while dishing out quality brews and fabulous bakes.

Settle into one of the cosy sofas and browse the selection of guest blends on cafetiere – Kenyan peaberry and Colombian La Manuela Supremo often feature – or plump for an expertly pulled espresso made with beans from Birkenhead roaster, Adams + Russell.

INSIDER'S TIP PAIR YOUR PICK WITH AN OLD-SCHOOL BACON SARNIE

Those partial to a chai latte will want to sample the house speciality barraquito: a fruity number from the Canary Islands made with condensed milk, two shots of espresso, steamed milk, cinnamon and orange syrup.

Expanding the coffee shop across the whole site this year will see craft fairs, weddings and live music events hosted in the quirky space.

ESTABLISHED
2016

KEY ROASTER
Adams + Russell

BREWING METHODS
Espresso, cafetiere

MACHINE
Expobar G10

GRINDER
Mazzer Super Jolly Timer

OPENING HOURS
Mon-Fri
9am-4pm
Sat 10am-4pm
Sun 8pm-11pm

Gluten FREE
ALTERNATIVE MILK
WIFI
OUTDOOR Seating
FAMILY FRIENDLY
DISABLED ACCESS
COFFEE COURSES

---

www.aspirationtrust.co.uk T: 01516 394918

f In Spire Coffee Bar @spirecoffeebar

MAP №30. CAFFÈ & CO

8 Dane Court, Rainhill, Prescot, Merseyside, L35 4LU

Schooling budding baristas in the art of coffee from his Rainhill cafe since 2011, professional filter buff and espresso slinger Neil Osthoff made things official this year on achieving SCA-qualified trainer status.

While Caffè & Co's courses previously occurred after opening hours, a new training lab – kitted out with the very latest brewing gear – now enables lessons to take place during both day and evening.

INSIDER'S TIP CHECK THE BLACKBOARD FOR SINGLE ORIGINS FROM A LEAGUE OF INDIE ROASTERS

For those happy to leave the latte art to the pros, there's a fine selection of indie roasters to choose from on the two La Marzocco machines, plus a comprehensive brew bar from which to sample the latest guest beans.

Pair your pourover pick with a couple of scoops of ice cream from the 80 strong collection, or plump for a crepe stuffed with sliced banana, Nutella and caramel.

And if something savoury is in order, you'll find a refreshing lunch menu filled with homemade seasonal soups, salads and sandwiches.

ESTABLISHED
2011

KEY ROASTER
Extract Coffee Roasters

BREWING METHODS
Espresso, V60, Chemex, AeroPress

MACHINES
La Marzocco Linea PB, La Marzocco GB5

GRINDERS
Victoria Arduino Mythos One Clima Pro x 2, Mahlkonig Vario

OPENING HOURS
Mon-Fri 8.30am-4.30pm
Sat 9am-4.30pm
Sun 10.30am-2.30pm

 Gluten FREE
 BEANS AVAILABLE INSTORE
 ALTERNATIVE MILK
 WIFI
 CYCLE FRIENDLY
 OUTDOOR SEATING
 FAMILY FRIENDLY
 DISABLED ACCESS
 BRING YOUR OWN CUP
 COFFEE COURSES

www.caffeandco.com T: 01514 932332
f Caffè & Co. 🐦 @caffeandco 📷 @caffe_and_co

MAP№31. KING STREET COFFEE COMPANY

1 Lord Street Arcade, Wrexham, North Wales, LL11 1LF

Bean-loving bros Phil and Andy Gallanders are a passionate pair of coffee-preneurs on a mission to caffeinate their home town of Wrexham.

Their cosy cafe is a classic example of contemporary coffee shop cool, with its suspended ceiling of electrical tray work and quality offering of Neighbourhood Coffee as espresso, V60 or batch brew. It's all a far cry from the brothers' former careers in commodity coffee.

INSIDER'S TIP TRY THE BANANA AND PECAN SLICE, BAKED BY ZANETA OF SIMPLY BAKES

'We're fairly chatty fellas so most of our regulars already know our story,' says Phil, who is proud to have opened the first speciality coffee shop in the town centre. *'Having previously worked in a large coffee chain, we not only wanted to expand our passion for and knowledge of coffee, but to share it with the people of our home town.'*

A second outpost in Wrexham has also opened: Bank Street Coffee will host events and continue the mission to promote the local independent community.

'We try our best to champion both great coffee and Wrexham,' adds Andy. *'There are a lot of great things happening here, so we take pride in promoting local events.'*

ESTABLISHED
2016

KEY ROASTER
Neighbourhood Coffee

BREWING METHODS
Espresso, V60, batch brew

MACHINE
Sanremo Verona TCS

GRINDER
Victoria Arduino Mythos One

OPENING HOURS
Mon-Fri
7am-6pm
Sat 8.30am-4pm

Gluten FREE

BEANS AVAILABLE
INSTORE

ALTERNATIVE MILK

WIFI

DISABLED ACCESS

www.kingstreetcoffee.co.uk   T: 01978 448818

f King Street Coffee Company   🐦 @kingstcoffee   📷 @kingstcoffeecompany

Frobishers

WE KNOW JUICE

**PREMIUM FRUIT JUICES AND JUICE DRINKS
AND CORDIALS PACKED FULL OF PERSONALITY**

01392 825333 | SALES@FROBISHERS.COM

WWW.FROBISHERS.COM | FOLLOW US @FROBISHERS

32. PROVIDERO
112 Upper Mostyn Street, Llandudno, Conwy, LL30 2SW

Big Prov, as it's affectionately known, is the not-so-little brother to the region's first speciality shop of the same name, and the offspring of a second successful crowdfunding campaign.

Swapping a mobile brew bar for his first permanent digs in 2014, owner Jon Hughes welcomed a second bricks and mortar venue to the Providero family at the beginning of 2017. *'We've gone from a man in a classic French van to a tiny shop, and now we have this beautiful big space too,'* enthuses Jon.

INSIDER'S TIP FEELING THE HEAT? THE ICED AEROPRESS IS THE BARISTAS' CHOICE IN SUMMER

Just like its sibling five miles down the road in Llandudno Junction, Big Prov crafts locally roasted Heartland coffee into silky smooth espresso, with at least three different beans to choose from on Wales' first Sanremo Opera machine. Guests such as Heart and Graft and Ancoats make appearances among the five-strong single origin offering on the brew bar.

Linger to sample the health-conscious foodie offerings such as pimped porridge and freshly baked sourdough, and to tickle the ivories of the baby grand.

ESTABLISHED
2017

KEY ROASTER
Heartland
Coffee Roasters

BREWING METHODS
Espresso,
AeroPress,
Clever Dripper,
batch brew,
syphon

MACHINE
Sanremo Opera

GRINDERS
Mythos One,
Mahlkonig EK 43

OPENING HOURS
Mon-Thu
8am-6pm
Fri 8am-9pm
Sat 9am-9pm
Sun 9am-5pm

 Gluten FREE
 BEANS AVAILABLE / INSTORE
 ALTERNATIVE MILK
 WiFi
 CYCLE FRIENDLY
 OUTDOOR seating
 FAMILY FRIENDLY
 DISABLED ACCESS
 COFFEE COURSES

www.providero.co.uk T: 01492 338220
f Providero Tea & Coffee House - Llandudno @providero @providero.tea.coffee

ROASTERS

> CROSBY COFFEE №42

MAP 33. CARVETII COFFEE

The Roastery, Threlkeld Business Park, Threlkeld, Cumbria, CA12 4SU

W ith Angharad Macdonald's roasting skills and Gareth Kemble's passion for researching ethically produced coffees, it's little wonder that Carvetii Coffee has grown beyond all expectations.

The roastery has won several awards, including *Cumbria Life*'s Best Small Producer, it's been cited in a list of top micro roasteries in *Caffeine* magazine, and its espresso blend and single origins – sold as whole beans, never ground coffee – are now served at cafes, hotels and restaurants across the UK.

ESTABLISHED
2011

ROASTER
MAKE & SIZE
Probat GN12
12 kg

COFFEE COURSES

BEANS AVAILABLE

ONLINE

'IN BEAN FORM, ONLY THE OUTSIDE OF THE COFFEE IS EXPOSED TO OXYGEN BUT WHEN GROUND, THE LARGER EXPOSED SURFACE AREA MEANS COFFEE DEGRADES QUICKER'

This year was particularly exciting for the pair as they branched out into larger premises. As well as having much better storage for green beans, they now have a roomy production area to facilitate even more retail growth, improved training facilities for customers and a workshop in which to service and repair espresso machines. Make sure to check out the calendar of home barista and brewing workshops too.

www.carvetiicoffee.co.uk   T: 01768 776979
f Carvetii Coffee   🐦 @carvetiicoffee   📷 @carvetiicoffee

No. **34.** RED BANK COFFEE ROASTERS

Unit 4b Lake Road Estate, Lake Road, Coniston, Cumbria, LA21 8EW

It's been a great year for Red Bank Coffee Roasters. From its base deep in the heart of the Lake District, the team have continued to grow a loyal, local client base, and started to pop up in revered retail spots such as Harvey Nichols and in top speciality coffee shops like Manchester's Grindsmith.

Their single origin Burundi Mpanga was recently featured in *Jamie* (Oliver) magazine and the Kenyan Kiriani featured as a Coffee of the Month in *Caffeine*.

Since opening the roastery two years ago, founder Tom Prestwich has stuck to his principles of sourcing the best ethically-produced coffee and roasting it to retain its unique characteristics. Red Bank also has a strong focus on sustainability and is notable for its use of biodegradable packaging.

ESTABLISHED
2015

ROASTER
MAKE & SIZE
Giesen W6A 6kg

BEANS AVAILABLE
ONSITE
ONLINE

'THE KENYAN KIRIANI FEATURED AS A COFFEE OF THE MONTH IN CAFFEINE'

'It's great to see all of our hard work starting to be recognised further afield,' says Tom. *'Our mission to source the best coffee possible while making the least impact will never change, but as we gain more experience I think we are getting better and better at it.'*

This year Tom also visited Rwanda, his first trip to origin, and has plans to visit Brazil and Ethiopia soon.

---

www.redbankcoffee.com   T: 07850 291171

f Red Bank Coffee Roasters   🐦 @redbankroasters   📷 @redbankroasters

MAP 35. MR DUFFIN'S COFFEE – THE COFFEE DEN

49 Main Street, Staveley, Kendal, Cumbria, LA8 9LN

Scenting the village of Staveley with the aroma of freshly roasted beans, Mr Duffin's has become a favourite for both beans and as a place to swing by for a coffee.

It's impossible to separate the roaster from the cafe, as the 15kg Giesen sits right in the middle of the store. It's separated from customers only by the bar at which you order your drinks, so you can watch Steven and Abbi cooking up the beans while you sit and sip.

STEVEN IS ENTHUSIASTIC ABOUT SUPPORTING LOCAL FARMERS AND USES STEPHENSONS FREE-RANGE MILK

Steven uses beans imported by a friend who works directly with a group of farmers in Peru. All the blends include Peruvian beans and are named after styles of talking (Chit Chat, Juicy Gossip and Shout Out) which refer to the origins of coffee houses. In addition, there is always a seasonal selection of single origin coffee available.

If you're in need of an additional pick me up, a homemade Coffee Buzz Ball hits the spot.

ESTABLISHED
2014

ROASTER
MAKE & SIZE
Giesen 15kg

CAFE
ONSITE

BEANS
AVAILABLE

ONSITE

ONLINE

---

www.mrduffinscoffee.com   T: 01539 822192

f Mr Duffins Coffee   🐦 @mrduffins   📷 @mr.duffins.coffee

ᴹᴬᴾ **36.** FARRER'S COFFEE

9 Shap Road Industrial Estate, Kendal, Cumbria, LA9 6NZ

'**W**e're the oldest indie coffee roastery in the UK,' say the guys at Farrer's Coffee in Kendal. It's an interesting take on the 200 year old roastery, which cooks up over three tonnes of coffee each week.

Hipster coffee accoutrements of the beard 'n' tats variety may be missing, but the family business has been keeping the North expertly caffeinated for two centuries. And as members of the Beverage Standards Association are committed to *'supporting customers to serve the best possible quality coffees.'*

ESTABLISHED
1819

ROASTER
MAKE & SIZE
Probat G60 60kg
Probatino 1.5kg
Vittoria 15kg

COFFEE
COURSES

BEANS
AVAILABLE
ONSITE

ONLINE

'WE'RE THE OLDEST INDIE COFFEE ROASTERY IN THE UK'

A trio of heavy duty roasters which includes a 15kg Vittoria, Probat G60 and Probatino 1.5kg do the honours, with greens from Brazil, Colombia, Guatemala, Ethiopia, Kenya, Vietnam, India, Tanzania, Costa Rica and Honduras used in the creation of 20 coffees. They also roast four seasonal speciality coffees (three single origin) at any time.

The roasting is complemented by barista skills training: in 2016 Farrer's opened a coffee school facility to provide a range of courses, including a City and Guilds in Barista Skills to existing customers and wannabe shot slingers.

www.farrerscoffee.co.uk   T: 01539 720020

f Farrers   🐦 @farrers_coffee

MAP 37. RINALDO'S SPECIALITY COFFEE & FINE TEA

Kendal, Cumbria.

'I think I offer one of the most flexible coffee subscription services in the UK,' smiles Rinaldo. 'Weekly, monthly, three monthly using pay-as-you-go or up-front-payment. There's even free local delivery in the Kendal area.'

Innovation and customer service are core to Rinaldo's coffee roasting business, which centres on the 15kg Giesen he bought via a crowdfunding campaign. The letterbox-friendly coffee packages travel to over a hundred postal customers, but you'll find his coffee in cafes and shops around the Lake District too.

ESTABLISHED
2015

ROASTER
MAKE & SIZE
Giesen 15kg

COFFEE COURSES

BEANS AVAILABLE
ONSITE

ONLINE

'WE AIM TO BREAK DOWN THE WALLS OF SPECIALITY SNOOTERY, WITHOUT DILUTING ANY OF THE QUALITY'

Italian by heritage and Cumbrian by birth, Rinaldo embraces the international nature of coffee and is dedicated to roasting only ethically sourced 100 per cent Arabica beans. Coffee fans who want to drop by and see it for themselves are very welcome and Rinaldo says: 'We love people to come to the roastery to try our coffee. We aim to break down the walls of speciality snootery, without diluting any of the quality or attention to detail.' A new barista training centre, serving takeaway drinks, is due to open in autumn 2017.

www.rinscoffee.com   T: 07947 093226
f Rinaldo's Speciality Coffee & Tea   🐦 @rinscoffee   📷 @rinscoffee

ᴺᵒ38. KIRCABI ROASTERS

18 Main Street, Kirkby Lonsdale, Carnforth, Lancashire, LA6 2AG

Kirkby Lonsdale is a smart little town, full of quality foodie finds. The only thing missing (until recently) was a coffee roastery, which is where Anthony Gatrell comes in.

In readiness to launch his first coffee business, the speciality-obsessed bean fiend got himself trained up at the London School of Coffee. He then took on a building with a little shopfront and moved his young family in upstairs to make his dream of becoming a full time roaster a reality.

'THE SPECIALITY-OBSESSED BEAN FIEND GOT HIMSELF TRAINED UP AT THE LONDON SCHOOL OF COFFEE'

A year on and there's a real buzz in Kirkby Lonsdale – and not just from the caffeine. Locals and visitors have nosed out Anthony's small batch roasting of single origins from around the world, and his seasonal espresso blend Art Store 18 has become a firm favourite in town.

Trading up from the current Toper Cafemino 1kg roaster to something more meaty, introducing new packaging and recruiting staff, Kircabi is starting to flourish.

Drop by to buy some beans and grab a takeaway coffee pulled through the sleek La Marzocco Linea Classic.

ESTABLISHED
2016

ROASTER
MAKE & SIZE
Toper Cafemino
1kg

BEANS AVAILABLE
ONSITE
ONLINE

www.kircabiroasters.co.uk   T: 07722 701713
f Kircabi Roasters   🐦 @kircabiroasters   📷 @kircabiroasters

MAP 39. ATKINSONS ROASTERY AND SHOP

10-12 China Street, Lancaster, Lancashire, LA1 1EX

A heady brew of heritage and avant garde is the secret to Atkinsons' success.

To experience the heritage, step into the fragrant shop and drink in the wall of beautifully battered coffee canisters bearing a patina from years of use, and salivate over the exquisitely wrapped chocolate from the distant shores of Madagascar and the Cote d'Ivoire.

Then sniff your way through the caddies (the team are very helpful) before getting your beans of choice weighed on original brass scales at the shop which has housed a roaster since 1837.

ESTABLISHED
1837

ROASTER
MAKE & SIZE
Loring Kestrel
35kg
Whitmee 56lb
Whitmee 28lb
Uno 14lb
Uno 7lb

CAFE
ONSITE

OPEN
TO THE PUBLIC

COFFEE
COURSES

BEANS
AVAILABLE

ONSITE

ONLINE

'I OFTEN GRAB CUSTOMERS AND DRAG THEM THROUGH THE BACK OF THE SHOP TO REVEAL THE FUTURISTIC, TARDIS-LIKE OPERATION'

The innovation may be a little more behind the scenes, but ask nicely and you're quite likely to get a quick tour of the light and airy new eco-build roastery with its shiny stainless steel Loring roaster flanked by two ancient Whitmees.

'I often grab interested customers and drag them through the shop to reveal the futuristic, TARDIS-like operation,' says Ian Steel. *'I'm aware that everyone cherishes our heritage but I like to surprise them with how progressive we are.'*

www.thecoffeehopper.com   T: 01524 65470
f Priory Hall   🐦 @coffeehopper   📷 @coffeehopper

MAP № 40. EXCHANGE COFFEE COMPANY

The Old Chapel Roastery, Islington, Canterbury Street, Blackburn, Lancashire, BB2 2HP

With more than 140 years' roasting experience between them, it's little surprise that the team at Exchange Coffee Company have created one of the North's most exciting speciality coffee empires, earning it 32 Great Taste Awards.

The Exchange experience is synonymous with brews across Blackburn as they have a coffee house and roasting shop in Fleming Square, a coffee bar in Blackburn Market and a van in The Mall. There's also a thriving wholesale roastery in a converted 1764 Baptist chapel and a new barista training school in the old Sunday school next door.

'WE SELECT AMAZING COFFEES OF DIFFERING VARIETALS, PROCESSING AND TERROIR'

The team are pleasingly particular and source single estate, Rainforest Alliance, organic and Fairtrade beans and have just started championing peaberry beans from Kenya, Brazil and Tanzania. *We select amazing coffees of differing varietals, processing and terroir,*' says Exchange's Richard Isherwood.

Working with Cimbali and Expobar, the team also offer plenty of advice, barista training and service backup for clients across the UK.

ESTABLISHED
2004

ROASTER
MAKE & SIZE
Probat GN25
25kg

OPEN
TO THE PUBLIC

COFFEE COURSES

BEANS AVAILABLE

www.exchangecoffee.co.uk T: 01254 665663

f Exchange Coffee Company 🐦 @exchange_coffee 📷 @exchange_coffee

MAP 41. ROBERTS & CO.

Cedar Farm, Back Lane, Mawdesley, Ormskirk, Lancashire, L40 3SY

With coffee flowing through their veins, it's no surprise that father and daughter team John and Amy Roberts know how to make green beans sing.

Since 1891, the Roberts family has been shipping tea from Liverpool's port (including supplying famous liners such as the Titanic).

From making waves in tea, they took on the coffee trade in 1930, bringing home beans from right across the equator before opening the first Roberts coffee shop in 1980.

Still a family affair, John and Amy run a unique roastery and espresso bar from an award winning farm building conversion in the West Lancashire countryside. From here they source and roast the finest single origin estate coffees and create outstanding espresso blends on their vintage English Whitmee roasters.

'THE ROBERTS FAMILY SUPPLIED TEA TO THE TITANIC'

Their reputation for creating remarkable coffee keeps the team busy, sending beans to restaurants, coffee shops and straight to purists' doors by mail order.

Taste the coffee at the espresso bar and see the open roastery in action, or visit their nearby cafe and pair your brew with a sensational homemade dish.

ESTABLISHED
1891

ROASTER
MAKE & SIZE
Whitmee
20kg
Whitmee
6kg

CAFE ONSITE

BEANS AVAILABLE
ONSITE
ONLINE

www.e-coffee.co.uk T: 01704 822433
f Roberts & Co Roastery @ @robertsco_coffee

42. CROSBY COFFEE

14 Bridge Road Industrial Estate, Litherland, Liverpool, Merseyside, L21 2QG

Jack Foster's mission to caffeinate the coffee lovers of Crosby and beyond started out with a tiny American-style roaster in his mum's living room. However, struggling to roast enough beans to keep up with demand, it wasn't long before he was able to ditch the day job in hospitality.

Today, Crosby Coffee supplies its Iron Men blend and selected single origin micro lots to independent coffee shops and restaurants across the UK. And, as head roaster, Jack now cooks up beans from Kenya, Honduras, Malawi, Guatemala, India and Nicaragua in a rather more substantial 10kg Toper.

ESTABLISHED
2013

ROASTER
MAKE & SIZE
Toper 10kg

COFFEE
COURSES

BEANS
AVAILABLE

ONSITE

ONLINE

'WE OFFER FREE BARISTA AND LATTE ART TRAINING TO ALL OUR WHOLESALE CUSTOMERS'

Crosby Coffee is also served in VIP areas at Aintree Racecourse, while its mocha brownie recipe features in *The Liverpool Cookbook*. It won Producer of the Year 2016 and Jack was a finalist for Young Business Person of the Year in the 2017 *Liverpool Echo* Business Awards.

'We offer barista training and are the Merseyside distributor for Cimbali,' says Jack. You don't have to be in the industry to get in on the action however; visit the brew bar for a quality brew and for beans to take home.

www.crosbycoffee.co.uk   T: 01515 385454
f Crosby Coffee   🐦 @coffeecrosby   📷 @crosbycoffeeltd

43. NEIGHBOURHOOD COFFEE

Unit 89, Chadwick Court, Chadwick Street, Liverpool, Merseyside, L3 7EY

Adding two new members to the team and doubling production to keep up with demand, it's been a busy third year for Chris and Ed, the duo behind Liverpool's first speciality coffee roaster.

The pair draw on years of coffee knowledge and trips to origin to form direct relationships with farms across the world.

'*I visited the Pererias this year, one family from an 11 family community called Sitio Jacutinga in Minas Gerais,*' explains Chris. '*From the trip we've secured a new Brazilian micro lot and are working on a project to improve processing quality and the price they can receive.*'

The Pereria beans feature in Neighbourhood's seasonal blend, a crowd pleasing smooth number with chocolatey tones. While one of Neighbourhood's two espresso blends offers a fruitier brew showcasing Ethiopia's signature citrus kick.

ESTABLISHED
2014

ROASTER
MAKE & SIZE
Giesen W15
15kg

OPEN
BY APPOINTMENT

COFFEE
COURSES

COURSES

BEANS
AVAILABLE

ONSITE

ONLINE

SAMPLE NEIGHBOURHOOD'S SELECTION OF SINGLE ORIGINS IN THE NEW RANGE OF NESPRESSO-COMPATIBLE CAPSULES

The guys offer training to wholesale customers including guidance on the latest La Marzocco kit, while burgeoning baristas can get in on the action with home brewing gear (online) and new home barista courses which are in the pipeline to launch this year.

www.neighbourhoodcoffee.co.uk   T: 01512 366741

f Neighbourhood Coffee   🐦 @nhoodcoffee   📷 @neighbourhoodcoffee

Get all our latest releases of fresh crop coffees delivered to your door with our Coffee Subscription now payable via monthly Direct Debit.

www.atkinsonscoffee.com

44. HEARTLAND COFFEE ROASTERS

Unit 3 Cwrt Roger Mostyn, Builder Street, Llandudno, Conwy, LL30 1DS

Flying the flag for speciality roasting in North Wales, Heartland is *'supporting local independent cafes by expanding people's experience of what speciality coffee can be,'* says roastery owner, Malcolm Klose.

'We love collaborating with other local businesses and exploring ways to incorporate quality coffee into what they produce'. The team has recently hooked up with local distillery Basecamp Liqueurs, to find the perfect bean and roast type for its hand roasted coffee liqueur and is also working with a local brewer, Wild Horse Brewing, to produce a nitro cold brew and a coffee beer.

'WE'RE WORKING WITH A LOCAL BREWER TO PRODUCE A NITRO COLD BREW AND A COFFEE BEER'

Roasting beans from every coffee producing region you could name, Heartland's latest thrills come in the form of the selection of a specific varietal, plot and processing method prior to harvest, and have just received the first shipment of Red Honey processed beans from Los Nogales in El Salvador.

'We've over 25 single origin coffees in stock, including direct-to-farm small batch speciality coffees from Honduras, Peru and Colombia,' says Malcolm. *'The Honduras makes a cracking cold brew.'*

ESTABLISHED
2012

ROASTER
MAKE & SIZE
Coffee-Tech
Ghibli 15kg

OPEN
BY APPOINTMENT

COFFEE
COURSES

BEANS
AVAILABLE
ONSITE

---

www.heartlandcoffi.co.uk   T: 01492 878757

f Heartlandcoffi   🐦 @heartlandcoffi   📷 @heartlandcoffi

GREATER MANCHESTER & CHESHIRE

> **MANCOCO COFFEE BAR & ROASTERY Nº52**

MERCED DEL POTRERO
MEXICO
Organic
£6.00 per 250g

MANCOCO
MANCHESTER BLEND
£5.50 per 250g

FINCA
CUATR
£6.00 p

PORVENIR ESTATE
COLOMBIA
£6.00 per 250g

SANTA LUCIA
AZ
Decaffeinated
per 250g

SANTA
BR
Rainfores
£6.00 p

MANCOCO
ESPRESSO BLEND
£5.50 per 250g

KAFFA FOREST ESTATE
ETHIOPIA
Rainforest Alliance & Organic
£6.00 per 250g

MONS
MALA
IND
£6.00 pe

Keighley

Blackpool

Lytham

Ripponden

Southport

Chorley

45

Littleborough
Rochdale

Horwich

Formby

Bolton

155

MANCHESTER
SEE CITY MAP OVERLEAF

Wigan

Leigh

176

53

Manchester

154

Glossop
Stockport

Warrington

54

Widnes

56

156

ell

57

157

55

Northwich

Macclesfield

Buxton

Chester

Buckley

143

Tarporley

Sandbach

Leek

144

Wrexham

Nantwich

Whitchurch

Cheadle

MANCHESTER

CAFE

46 Takk Coffee House
47 Foundation Coffee House
48 Fig + Sparrow
49 Federal Cafe & Bar
50 Pot Kettle Black
51 Grindsmith Espresso & Brewbar
52 ManCoCo Coffee Bar & Roastery

MORE GOOD CUPS

146 Popup Bikes
147 Another Heart To Feed
148 Grindsmith - The Pod
149 Teacup Kitchen
150 North Tea Power
151 Idle Hands
152 Ezra & Gil
153 Ancoats Coffee Co.

MORE GOOD ROASTERS

173 Heart and Graft Coffee Roastery
174 Ancoats Coffee Co.
175 ManCoCo

45. THE SNUG COFFEE HOUSE

67a Market Street, Atherton, Manchester, M46 0DA

After 20 years in insurance, Rachael Flaszczak was ready for a change of career. And, identifying a gap in the coffee market in Atherton, she took a leap of faith and set up shop.

'My mission was to create an alternative place for people to come and enjoy a good brew, get lost in a book and chat, with a real social vibe,' Rachael enthuses.

INSIDER'S TIP ENJOY THE SUNTRAP COURTYARD WITH ITS FLOWERS, HERBS AND APPLE TREE

With paisley carpets, walls decked with artwork and crates full of handmade goods, The Snug is utterly unique. One wall is dedicated to local crafts and produce for sale, and the community spirit is reinforced through the many events which take place – from knitting and networking to DJ nights. Rachael spent a long time researching roasters and says: *'In the end, I went to Liverpool-based Joe Black and haven't looked back. For the past three years we've been through coffee training programmes and have kept up with what's on-trend by attending cupping festivals.'*

You'll also find over 30 loose-leaf teas, syrups, milkshakes, gins, wines and real ales.

ESTABLISHED
2015

KEY ROASTER
Joe Black Coffee

BREWING METHODS
Espresso, filter, Chemex

MACHINE
Iberital

GRINDER
Iberital

OPENING HOURS
Mon-Sat
8am-4pm
(later for events)

 Gluten FREE

 BEANS AVAILABLE INSTORE

 ALTERNATIVE MILK

 WIFI

 CYCLE FRIENDLY

 OUTDOOR SEATING

 FAMILY FRIENDLY

 DISABLED ACCESS

www.thesnugatherton.com   T: 01942 875430

f The Snug Coffee House   🐦 @snugatherton   📷 @thesnugatherton

№46. TAKK COFFEE HOUSE

6 Tariff Street, Manchester, M1 2FF

'Takk was created to provide a friendly coffee space, rooted in our community,' says owner Philip Hannaway. And it's the welcoming team, helping coffee fans choose beans they'll love, that's one of the draws at this hip Northern Quarter hangout.

There are certainly plenty of options for the baristas to pick from, with house roast Clifton complemented by a selection from Coffee Collective, Bonanza, Five Elephant, Vertical and Talor&Jørgen.

INSIDER'S TIP A SECOND TAKK WILL OPEN IN 2018 AT THE UNIVERSITY OF MANCHESTER CAMPUS

Closely involved with Clifton's coffee farming partners, Philip says, 'We are proud of our direct relationship with our coffee producer in El Salvador, and are also having a lot of fun working with other leading roasters across the world.'

Complementing Takk's commitment to quality growers and roasters is the use of local produce in its food menu. This includes milk from a free-range herd at Stephensons Dairy in Lancashire, bread from Pollen Bakery and meat from W H Frost butchers in the city.

ESTABLISHED
2013

KEY ROASTER
Clifton Coffee Roasters

BREWING METHODS
Espresso, Chemex, AeroPress, cold brew

MACHINE
La Marzocco Linea PB

GRINDERS
Mythos, Mahlkonig K30, Mahlkonig EK 43

OPENING HOURS
Mon-Fri
8am-5pm
Sat 9am-5pm
Sun 10am-5pm

 Gluten FREE

 BEANS AVAILABLE INSTORE

 ALTERNATIVE MILK

 WIFI

 CYCLE FRIENDLY

OUTDOOR SEATING

 FAMILY FRIENDLY

 BRING YOUR OWN Cup

www.takkmcr.com T: 07989 583576
f Takk @takkmcr @takkmcr

MAP № 47. FOUNDATION COFFEE HOUSE

Sevendale House, Lever Street, Northern Quarter, Manchester, M1 1JB

Indecisive drinkers should swot up on the menu before brunch at this Manchester meeting space, as whatever your poison – speciality espresso, single estate hot chocolate or something stronger – the options are almost endless.

Wild card coffee choices such as bulletproof (black coffee with butter and coconut oil), kevlar (black coffee and coconut oil) and Vietnamese ca phe offer an intriguing alternative to the familiar flat white.

More conventional caffeine kicks from Cornish roaster Origin come in a selection of serve styles, from V60 to syphon, thanks to Foundation's brushed-up baristas.

INSIDER'S TIP LOOK OUT FOR UPCOMING COFFEE COURSES WITH HEAD BARISTA HANNAH MITCHELL

Lunchtime staples take an international tour of the latest trends, from the pastrami, mustard and dill pickle sarnie to the salmon and quinoa salad with sun-dried tomatoes and mixed leaves. Follow that with Tyler and Hall's vegan brownies or indulge in an In Truffles We Trust luxurious brownie.

Decisions don't stop once you've ordered, as a collection of seating areas suits every caffeine occasion, while the Foundation Store's coffee merch will have you assessing how much you can haul home.

ESTABLISHED
2015

KEY ROASTER
Origin Coffee Roasters

BREWING METHODS
Espresso, V60, Chemex, AeroPress, batch brew

MACHINE
La Marzocco Linea PB ABR

GRINDERS
Nuova Simonelli Mythos One, Mahlkonig EK 43

OPENING HOURS
Mon-Tue
7.30am-7pm
Wed-Fri
7.30am-10pm
Sat 9am-10pm
Sun 12pm-6pm

www.foundationcoffeehouse.co.uk T: 01612 388633

f Foundation Coffee House 🐦 @fdncoffee 📷 @fdncoffee

MAP 48. # FIG + SPARROW

20 Oldham Street, Northern Quarter, Manchester, M1 1JN

From outside, this creative space in Manchester's Northern Quarter may look snug, but step over the threshold at Fig + Sparrow and you'll discover an Aladdin's cave of interior inspo and coffee culture.

A reshuffle of the shop floor in 2016 saw the brew bar relocated to the back wall, making way for a bunch of new booths and an extended lunch menu which is now etched on wooden boards.

INSIDER'S TIP — DODGING DAIRY? PICK FROM A WIDE SELECTION OF MILK ALTERNATIVES

Grab a table and sample the espresso blend from Climpson & Sons or their latest seasonal single origin, The Fields, on filter. And if you've got food on order, browse the aspirational homewares while you wait.

From designer door knobs to sustainable soap, the lustworthy line-up of treasures to take home also extends to freshly baked Trove bread, gluten-free brownies and salted caramel millionaire's shortbread.

ESTABLISHED
2013

KEY ROASTER
Climpson
& Sons

BREWING METHODS
Espresso,
AeroPress, V60,
Chemex

MACHINE
La Marzocco
Linea PB

GRINDERS
Victoria Arduino
Mythos One,
Mahlkonig EK 43

OPENING HOURS
Mon-Fri
8am-7pm
Sat 9am-6pm
Sun 10am-6pm

 Gluten FREE

 BEANS AVAILABLE INSTORE

 ALTERNATIVE MILK

 WIFI

 CYCLE FRIENDLY

 OUTDOOR SEATING

 FAMILY FRIENDLY

 DISABLED ACCESS

 BRING YOUR OWN CUP

www.figandsparrow.co.uk   T: 07815 137563

f Fig + Sparrow   🐦 @figsparrow   📷 @figsparrow

MAP 49. FEDERAL CAFE & BAR

9 Nicholas Croft, Manchester, M4 1EY

Espresso martinis may have gone mainstream, but the wickedly smooth thrills of the caffeinated cocktail have been seducing visitors to Federal since 2014.

Of course, the Ozone coffee that's skillfully combined with vodka and Mr Black liqueur in the Federal Martini (or banana liqueur and salted caramel in the banoffee version) is also served sans booze.

INSIDER'S TIP ASK FOR THE LATEST PICK OF THE SEASONAL SINGLE ORIGINS BEHIND THE BAR

'Visiting Aussies often say it's the best coffee they've had in the UK,' enthuses owner Emily Ribeiro.

And the Melbourne-inspired brunch plates, Bundaberg bottles and Anzac biscuits at the Antipodean-style bar probably play a part in their approval, too.

The kitchen's daily specials go like hot cakes, while Emily's toasted banana bread with vanilla mascarpone, and the halloumi and 'shrooms with extra chorizo are trusted trailblazers. Whichever you choose, it'll go beautifully with a cheeky brunch bevvy or a velvety flat white.

ESTABLISHED
2014

KEY ROASTER
Ozone Coffee Roasters

BREWING METHODS
Espresso, V60, AeroPress, cold brew, filter

MACHINE
La Marzocco Linea PB

GRINDERS
Mazzer Robur, Mahlkonig EK 43

OPENING HOURS
Mon-Fri
7.30am-6pm
Sat 8am-6pm
Sun 8am-5pm

Gluten FREE

BEANS AVAILABLE INSTORE

ALTERNATIVE MILK

WIFI

CYCLE FRIENDLY

OUTDOOR SEATING

www.federalcafe.co.uk   T: 01614 250974

f Federal Cafe & Bar   🐦 @federalcafebar   📷 @federalcafebar

MAP№ 50. POT KETTLE BLACK

Barton Arcade, Deansgate, Manchester, M3 2BW

For a break from industrial chic decor – there's a limit to how much Edison bulb lighting and polished concrete a coffee fan can take – the vintage charm of Pot Kettle Black provides a refreshing alternative.

Cosily installed in Manchester's Victorian Barton Arcade, its high ceilings, oil lamps, vintage wooden tables and a signature splash of PKB red create an attractive setting in which to revel in quality caffeine and award winning food.

INSIDER'S TIP
COFFEE DATE? COSY UP WITH AN 18oz FILTER FOR TWO

Though the style may be classic, the coffee offering is bang up-to-date with a range of brewing methods that includes cold brew and V60.

The kitchen follows suit with a bill of eye-catching breakfasts and innovative lunch dishes that are perfectly packaged for your Instagram feed. The 'nduja eggs and Korean chicken sub are particularly pleasing.

Plans to expand this popular people-watching spot are under way, with a new craft bakery and a co-working and events space to launch late 2017.

ESTABLISHED
2014

KEY ROASTER
Workshop Coffee

BREWING METHODS
Espresso, drip, cold brew, V60, AeroPress

MACHINE
La Marzocco Linea PB

GRINDERS
Mahlkonig Mythos One, Mahlkonig EK 43

OPENING HOURS
Mon-Sat
8am-7pm
Sun 9am-5pm

 Gluten FREE

 BEANS AVAILABLE INSTORE

 ALTERNATIVE MILK

 WIFI

 CYCLE FRIENDLY

 OUTDOOR seating

 FAMILY FRIENDLY

 DISABLED ACCESS

 BRING YOUR OWN cup

www.potkettleblackltd.co.uk   T: 07752 752448
f Pot Kettle Black Ltd   🐦 @pkbcoffee   📷 @pkbcoffee

51. GRINDSMITH ESPRESSO & BREWBAR

231-233 Deansgate, Manchester, M3 4EN

Grindsmith's original espresso bar on Deansgate has been a hub for the city's creatives and desk hoppers since it opened in 2014. Previously home to just 25 seats, recent expansion has allowed the co-working cafe concept with Manchester Rise to flourish further.

However, it's not just keyboard warriors and pencil pushers flocking to the industrial chic coffee shop for flawless flat whites and killer filters. Pre 9am you'll find a queue of connoisseurs picking up a Heart and Graft hit to-go, while monthly music events attract an even wider pool of Mancunians to the speciality bar.

INSIDER'S TIP PLANNING A MEETING? BOOK A SEMINAR ROOM FOR BONUS BOSS BROWNIE POINTS

A trophy case of crisp croissants, stellar traybakes and stacked sandwiches are complemented by a comprehensive range of brewing gear, including the more unusual syphon. Occasional cupping sessions and other ad-hoc events pop up after dark, so keep a check on Grindsmith's Insta account for updates.

And don't forget to drop by for a brew at the Grindsmith Pod, a stylish summerhouse coffee haven in Greengate Square.

ESTABLISHED
2014

KEY ROASTER
Heart and Graft
Coffee Roastery

BREWING METHODS
Espresso, Kalita
Wave, syphon,
Chemex, filter,
AeroPress,
cold brew

MACHINE
Black Eagle

GRINDERS
Mythos,
Mahlkonig EK 43

OPENING HOURS
Mon-Fri
8am-8pm
Sat 9am-6pm
Sun 10am-6pm

BEANS AVAILABLE INSTORE

ALTERNATIVE MILK

WIFI

CYCLE FRIENDLY

FAMILY FRIENDLY

DISABLED ACCESS

BRING YOUR OWN CUP

www.grindsmith.com   T: 01614 084699

f Grindsmith   🐦 @grindsmith_gn   📷 @grindsmith_deansgate

MAP № 52. MANCOCO COFFEE BAR & ROASTERY

Arch 84, Hewitt Street, Manchester, M15 4GB

If you're exploring the up-and-coming cultural quarter at the end of Deansgate, you'll probably smell ManCoCo before you find it.

Tucked away underneath the railway arches, this micro roaster was one of the first speciality roasters in the city centre.

In 2015 Darren and Stuart added a little artisan coffee bar to the premises, so customers can sit and sip ManCoCo coffees while the business of roasting takes place just a couple of metres away.

INSIDER'S TIP VISIT ON A ROASTING DAY TO SEE AND SMELL THE MAGIC TAKE PLACE

Specialising in hand-roasting traceable and ethically-sourced green coffees from around the world, the ManCoCo team only cook up small batches, so freshness is ensured.

It's not all about the coffee either, as they've recently added a selection of beautiful, organic estate teas which are ethically sourced via Storm Tea.

Bean or leaf, you won't go wrong if you pair your pick with a locally made traybake – and don't forget to grab a bag of beans to take home.

ESTABLISHED
2012

KEY ROASTER
ManCoCo

BREWING METHODS
Espresso, filter, V60

MACHINE
La Marzocco GB5

GRINDERS
Anfim Super Caimano, Mahlkonig K30 twin, Mahlkonig Tanzania

OPENING HOURS
Mon-Fri
7.30am-4pm
Sat 8.30am-5pm

BEANS AVAILABLE INSTORE

ALTERNATIVE MILK

WIFI

CYCLE FRIENDLY

DISABLED ACCESS

BRING YOUR OWN Cup

---

www.mancoco.co.uk   T: 01612 371916
f ManCoCo   🐦 @mancocoltd   📷 @mancocoltd

MAP 53. GRINDSMITH MEDIA CITY

Unit 5-6, The Garage, Media City UK, Salford, Greater Manchester, M50 2EQ

To locate the holy grail of speciality in Manchester's slickest suburb, simply look for the vibrant stained glass window among Media City's shiny skyscrapers. The locally crafted panes (inspired by a trip to Honduras) celebrate coffee farming and form a pleasing contrast to the contemporary interior of Grindsmith's second set-up.

A collection of brewing kit behind the custom bar not only complements the sleek style but fashions fantastic filters from a roster of guest roasters which includes Ancoats, The Barn and Red Bank. On the custom white Black Eagle espresso machine, the team sling shots using beans from Heart and Graft.

INSIDER'S TIP A CRACKING COCKTAIL AND CRAFT BEER LIST MAKES THIS A POST 4PM PIT-STOP

Brunch is served until four and fuels the throng of worker bees grabbing avo on toast and pastrami-packed sandwiches en route to their next meeting, as well as those who want to settle in for french toast with macerated strawberries, vanilla mascarpone and berry coulis.

ESTABLISHED
2016

KEY ROASTER
Heart and Graft
Coffee Roastery

BREWING METHODS
Espresso, Kalita
Wave, Chemex,
filter, bulk brew

MACHINE
Black Eagle

GRINDERS
Mythos,
Mahlkonig EK 43

OPENING HOURS
Mon-Sat
7.30am-6pm

BEANS AVAILABLE INSTORE

ALTERNATIVE MILK

WIFI

CYCLE FRIENDLY

OUTDOOR seating

FAMILY friendly

DISABLED ACCESS

BRING YOUR OWN Cup.

---

www.grindsmith.com T: 01614 084699

f Grindsmith 🐦 @grindsmith_mc 📷 @grindsmith_mediacity

54. CAFFEINE AND CO

Longford Park, Manchester, M32 8DA

T ake a stroll through Manchester's Longford Park to light upon Caffeine and Co, one of the city's little treasures.

'Our identity revolves around freshness,' says owner Phil Howells, explaining that all food is made daily on site. With two rounds of bread-making each day, customers are guaranteed a loaf so oven fresh that it's often too hot to slice. You won't mind waiting around for it to cool though, not with the quality of coffee on offer.

INSIDER'S TIP GRAB A SEAT OUTSIDE AND GET YOUR FIX ALFRESCO

Caffeine and Co proudly asserts the distinction of being the first cafe in Manchester to go solely single origin. Cornwall roaster Origin provides Caffeine's customers with sweet caramel and milk chocolate flavours via its South American beans, which are mostly served as espresso based drinks (it's great with milk). Go V60 if you're after a cleaner, filtered brew.

Bringing world-class coffee thrills and cake to the city of Manchester is the lofty aim. And how do they manage it? *'We do the simple things really well,'* says Phil.

We'll raise a flattie to that.

ESTABLISHED
2013

KEY ROASTER
Origin Coffee
Roasters

BREWING METHODS
Espresso, V60

MACHINE
Nuova Simonelli
T3

GRINDERS
Mythos One,
Mahlkonig EK 43

OPENING HOURS
Mon-Fri
10am-5pm
Sat
9.45am-5pm
Sun
10am-5pm

Gluten FREE

BEANS AVAILABLE INSTORE

ALTERNATIVE MILK

WIFI

CYCLE FRIENDLY

OUTDOOR seating

FAMILY friendly

DISABLED ACCESS

BRING YOUR OWN Cup

COFFEE COURSES AVAILABLE

T: 07778 784440
f Caffeine & Co 🐦 @caffeineandco

MAP 55. NOOK NEIGHBOURHOOD COFFEE

111 Heaton Moor Road, Heaton Moor, Stockport, Cheshire, SK4 4HY

In addition to laid-back vibes and an awesome soundtrack, Nook is known for its witty blackboard scribblings, the reclaimed-door ceiling and an on-the-side movie rental service.

Now almost two years old, the cafe's aim to produce 'speciality coffee, ground to order and made with love' has become a reality. And with a band of beans in the hopper from the likes of Ancoats and North Star, there's plenty of caffeinated affection to go round.

INSIDER'S TIP
LOOK OUT FOR REGULAR FOODIE POP-UP EVENTS

The recently expanded kitchen has given rise to a delectable new menu for homemade thrills at breakfast, brunch and lunch. Expect plenty of local fare; these guys are firm supporters of Stockport's food producers.

If the speciality coffee and stonking grub isn't enough, check out the service for four-legged visitors: Nook provides personalised mugs for pooches so you can take your mutt for a macchiato.

ESTABLISHED
2015

KEY ROASTER
North Star
Coffee Roasters

BREWING METHODS
Espresso, V60,
Chemex,
AeroPress,
cold brew

MACHINE
La Marzocco
2 AV

GRINDERS
Mahlkonig,
Mazzer

OPENING HOURS
Mon-Fri
8.30am-5pm
Sat 8.30am-6pm
Sun 9am-5pm

Gluten FREE

BEANS AVAILABLE INSTORE

ALTERNATIVE MILK

WIFI

CYCLE FRIENDLY

OUTDOOR SEATING

FAMILY FRIENDLY

BRING YOUR OWN CUP

---

www.nooknc.co.uk T: 01614 325385
f Nook Neighbourhood Coffee 🐦 @thenooknc 📷 @thenooknc

MAP 56. COFFEE FIX

80 Church Road, Gatley, Cheadle, Greater Manchester, SK8 4NQ

From lycra-clad wheel worshippers powering up with an espresso hit, to frazzled mums and dads nurturing the next generation of coffee lovers, moments of calm are rare at this buzzing community hub in Gatley.

Since launching their spacious coffee shop six years ago, siblings Gareth and Claira have garnered a lively local following for their blend of Manchester-roasted coffee and busy little kitchen.

And its location, a short detour from Cheshire's scenic walks and riding routes, results in an ever-expanding crop of Coffee Fix fans.

Fuelling the bulk of the activity are beautiful beans from Heart and Graft, while guest roasters such as Passion Fruit keep the V60 and AeroPress wheels turning.

INSIDER'S TIP DON YOUR CYCLING GEAR AND GET 10% OFF SPECIAL MENU ADDITIONS

Hearty homemade food includes an inventive vegan brekkie of polenta wedges, baked beans, avo, tomatoes and beetroot, while stuffed flat breads are a Fix fave – we're all over the halloumi and sweet chilli.

A calendar of street food pop-ups joins the busy schedule of social events this year; it's the perfect excuse to browse the local craft beer and wine selection.

ESTABLISHED
2011

KEY ROASTER
Heart and Graft
Coffee Roastery

BREWING METHODS
Espresso,
AeroPress, V60

MACHINE
Conti Monte
Carlo

GRINDER
Compak E8

OPENING HOURS
Mon-Sat
9am-4.30pm
Sun
10am-4.30pm

 Gluten FREE

 BEANS AVAILABLE INSTORE

 ALTERNATIVE MILK

 WIFI

 CYCLE FRIENDLY

 OUTDOOR seating

 FAMILY FRIENDLY

 DISABLED ACCESS

 BRING YOUR OWN Cup

www.wearecoffeefix.com T: 01612 820090
f Coffee Fix 🐦 @coffee_fix 📷 @wearecoffeefix

57. COMMON GROUND

20 Shaw's Road, Altrincham, Greater Manchester, WA14 1QU

One for the Lycra-clad hobbyists on their next tour through Altrincham, this newbie on the Manchester coffee block comes from a trio of coffee enthusiasts who are also former Olympians.

In summer 2016, Liam Phillips (BMX), Jess Varnish (cycling) and Fran Halsall (swimming) were representing Team GB in Rio; by June 2017 the friends were putting the finishing touches to their first coffee shop and kitchen.

INSIDER'S TIP: HIT THE URBAN GARDEN WITH AN ICED FILTER AND COLOURFUL SALAD

Globetrotting introduced the athletes to the world of speciality coffee, and international influences are reflected in the relaxed Scandi interior, Antipodean-style coffee and tropical decor.

'There are lots of places serving great coffee in Manchester,' says manager Bobby McNicol. 'And while we'd like to be recognised as one of the best, we're more passionate about the development of the speciality coffee scene in Manchester's outer suburbs.'

Secure a spot on the cosy, cushioned window bench and sample the latest beans from London-based Caravan while perusing the menu for a breakfast of champions.

ESTABLISHED
2017

KEY ROASTER
Caravan Coffee Roasters

BREWING METHODS
Espresso, V60, AeroPress, batch brew

MACHINE
Victoria Arduino VA388 Black Eagle

GRINDERS
Victoria Arduino Mythos One, Mahlkonig EK 43

OPENING HOURS
Tue-Sun
8am-6pm

 Gluten FREE

 BEANS AVAILABLE INSTORE

 ALTERNATIVE MILK

 WiFi

 CYCLE FRIENDLY

 OUTDOOR seating

 FAMILY FRIENDLY

www.commongroundalt.co.uk   T: 07478 790009

f Common Ground   🐦 @commongroundalt   📷 @commongroundalt

NORTH AND WEST YORKSHIRE

> **THE CURIOUS COFFEE COMPANY** №62

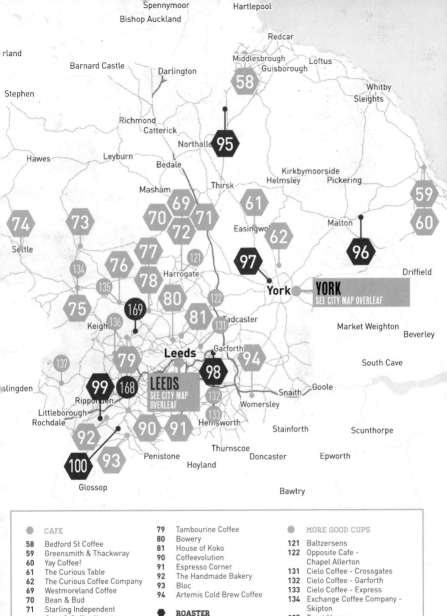

LEEDS

YORK

MAP 58. BEDFORD ST COFFEE

27 Bedford Street, Middlesbrough, North Yorkshire, TS1 2LL

Laptop lingerers, coffee-philes and drooping shoppers alike find solace in this stylish space in the heart of Middlesbrough. Swing by for a swig of the good stuff and you won't be disappointed by the choice on offer.

An array of its own Rounton single origin espressos, alongside guest filters from European roasters White Label and Five Elephant, mean there is always something gratifyingly good in the hopper. And you can be safe in the knowledge that every coffee bean originates from a sustainable source.

Similarly, ingredients in the inviting menu of cakes, bakes and bagels are sourced from indie neighbourhood enterprises.

INSIDER'S TIP DON'T MISS THE LEGENDARY MONTHLY COMEDY NIGHTS

'We're dedicated to quality and sustainability and want to contribute positively to our local economy,' says owner David Beattie. 'Fiercely independent ourselves, we only buy from independent suppliers.'

And as you'd expect with a Rounton cafe, not only are the staff bean buffs, they're also skilled latte artists – barista Danielle Grey recently made it to the finals of Manchester's Ladies Who Latte.

ESTABLISHED
2013

KEY ROASTER
Rounton Coffee Roasters

BREWING METHODS
V60, AeroPress

MACHINE
Sanremo Verona RS

GRINDERS
Mahlkonig EK 43, Mahlkonig K30 Vario

OPENING HOURS
Mon-Fri 8am-5pm
Sat 9am-5pm
Sun 10am-4pm

 Gluten FREE

 BEANS AVAILABLE INSTORE

 ALTERNATIVE MILK

 WIFI

 OUTDOOR Seating

 FAMILY Friendly

 DISABLED ACCESS

COFFEE COURSES

www.rountoncoffee.co.uk T:01642 647856

f Bedford St Coffee   @bedfordstcoffee   @bedfordstcoffee

59. GREENSMITH & THACKWRAY

30 St Nicholas Street, Scarborough, North Yorkshire, YO11 2HF

This former gentlemen's outfitters with its original gold leaf lettering is steeped in history, but owners Jack and Josh have breathed new life into it, refashioning the space into a slick speciality coffee shop and social hub.

'We knew that it wasn't enough to just serve great coffee,' explains Jack. *'And we wanted to do it in a location that was truly different and unique to our town.'*

INSIDER'S TIP TAKE PART IN ONE OF THE CUPPING AND TRAINING SESSIONS

The result is a wealth of Instagram opportunities at every turn: from the pared-back industrial design to the uncluttered lunch menu of wholesome salads and handcrafted ciabattas, and bevy of homebaked beauties on the counter.

Of course coffee is the star attraction and, in addition to the house espresso from Dark Woods, there's a Colombian Finca El Tormento on batch brew and a fruity nitro number from Maude.

Opening hours are soon to be extended so that local craft beers and distilleries can also get their moment of glory on the custom bar.

ESTABLISHED
2014

KEY ROASTER
Dark Woods
Coffee

BREWING METHODS
Espresso,
batch brew,
nitro cold brew

MACHINE
Cimbali M100

GRINDERS
Cimbali
Magnum on
demand,
Mahlkonig Vario

OPENING HOURS
Mon-Sat
9am-5pm

Gluten FREE

BEANS AVAILABLE INSTORE

ALTERNATIVE MILK

FAMILY FRIENDLY

DISABLED ACCESS

COFFEE COURSES

www.greensmiththackwray.com

f Greensmith & Thackway   🐦 @greensmiththack   📷 @greensmiththack

№ 60. YAY COFFEE!

12a York Place, Scarborough, North Yorkshire, YO11 2NP

As the name of this compact little cafe suggests, Lottie and Rob McFarlane's enthusiasm for coffee (and life) is joyously exuberant.

Their warm community spirit is embodied in the colourful Polaroids that adorn the walls, and the twinkling fairy lights draped around the 'communal happiness board' – a collage of quotes, pictures and jokes.

It's no wonder the cafe is a hub for shoppers, coffee fiends and freelancers with laptops.

INSIDER'S TIP   LOOK OUT FOR REGULAR PUBLIC CUPPINGS, EVENTS AND PROMOTIONS

A wall map illustrating the provenance of the beans of the day is your first sign that the team are serious about sourcing the good stuff.

The second is an ever changing blackboard of single origin filter, espresso based and nitro coffees, enabling regulars to drink their way around the equator.

Coffee is complemented by single origin hot chocolate, a range of teas and cold drinks. And if you're after some Scarborough fayre (sorry), try the menu of bagels, cakes and nibbles.

ESTABLISHED
2015

KEY ROASTER
Extract
Coffee Roasters

BREWING METHODS
Espresso, V60

MACHINE
Sanremo
Verona RS

GRINDERS
Mahlkonig K30,
Mahlkonig EK 43

OPENING HOURS
Mon-Fri
8am-6pm
Sat 9am-5pm

Gluten FREE

BEANS AVAILABLE
INSTORE

ALTERNATIVE MILK

WIFI

CYCLE FRIENDLY

COFFEE COURSES

www.yaycoffee.com   T: 01723 364133

f Yay Coffee Scarborough   🐦 @yaycoffeeuk   📷 @yaycoffeeuk

MAP 61. THE CURIOUS TABLE

2 Market Place, Easingwold, York, North Yorkshire, YO61 3AG

It doesn't take a genius to decipher why Eddie Copley-Farnell called his York cafe The Curious Table. Cast your eyes downwards and you'll notice that each table base is a quirky piece of upcycled art, fashioned from anything from an old industrial drill to a railway sleeper and track.

The unique touches don't stop there. With every cup of coffee served, you'll get a complimentary bite-size brownie. The trademark freebie is a sweet pairing to the house blend that's carefully roasted on the outskirts of town at York Coffee Emporium.

INSIDER'S TIP EXPLORE AN ARRAY OF WORLD CUISINE AT THE REGULAR POP-UP EVENTS

Since opening in 2013, the cafe has built a loyal fan base for lunches, sharing platters and takeaways, with plenty of options for gluten and dairy dodgers. Get there early at breakfast to avoid table scrums – dippy eggs with an army of soldiers and homemade scones are just two delicious ways to start the day.

In summer, take brekkie outdoors and enjoy alfresco coffee slurping, nestled into a bean bag on the green.

ESTABLISHED
2013

KEY ROASTER
York Coffee Emporium

BREWING METHODS
Espresso, french press

MACHINE
Cimbali Casadio

GRINDER
Cimbali Casadio

OPENING HOURS
Mon-Fri 7.30am-5pm
Sat 8.30am-4pm
Sun 9.30am-3pm

 Gluten FREE
 BEANS AVAILABLE INSTORE
 ALTERNATIVE MILK
 WIFI
 CYCLE FRIENDLY
 OUTDOOR SEATING
 FAMILY FRIENDLY
 BRING YOUR OWN

120

www.thecurioustable.co.uk   T: 01347 823434
f The Curious Table   🐦 @thecurioustable

Photos: Dominic Wright Photography

MAP № 62. THE CURIOUS COFFEE COMPANY

8 Haxby Shopping Centre, Haxby, York, North Yorkshire, YO32 2LU

'*Coffee is our passion and great service a way of life,*' is the motto at this new addition to The Curious Table family.

Launched in March 2017, the second speciality shop in the Curious collection is already making its mark in Haxby as a popular stop for breakfast, lunch and coffee (served with its signature brownie on the side).

INSIDER'S TIP   TRY ONE OF THE FAMED CHOCOLATE BROWNIES WARM WITH ICE CREAM

Beans are roasted at nearby York Coffee Emporium before the team fashions fabulous flat whites and espresso on the tech-tastic Cimbali machine. Loose-leaf fans can enjoy their bevvy Japanese-style in delightful tetsubin teapots.

If you're not partisan to gluten or dairy, this friendly cafe has plenty of goodies for you, and the staff are happy to adapt dishes.

'*Most people don't even realise the brownies and churros (inspired by a recent trip to New Zealand) are made using gluten-free flour as they're so delicious,*' smiles owner Eddie Copley-Farnell.

ESTABLISHED
2017

KEY ROASTER
York Coffee Emporium

BREWING METHODS
Espresso, french press

MACHINES
Cimbali

GRINDERS
Cimbali Magnum

OPENING HOURS
Mon-Fri
7.30am-5pm
Sat 8.30am-4pm

Gluten FREE

BEANS AVAILABLE INSTORE

ALTERNATIVE MILK

WIFI

CYCLE FRIENDLY

FAMILY FRIENDLY

DISABLED ACCESS

BRING YOUR OWN Cup

`4 765158

...us Coffee Company   🐦 @curiouscoffeeed   📷 @thecuriouscoffeecompany

63. BREW & BROWNIE

5 Museum Street, York, North Yorkshire, YO1 7DT

Doing exactly what it says on the tin, this aptly named merchant of gooeyness is your go-to for an unmissable brownie served with a beautiful brew from Bristol's Extract.

There's more to it than that, of course, but hey, it's a helluva way to start. Next on your hit list should be an American pancake stack, for which fans travel from miles around. Pimped with the likes of banana and salted caramel, or fruit, yogurt and honey, as well as the good ol' maple syrup, streaky bacon and blueberries, you'll need to make a return visit to indulge *all* your pancake fantasies.

INSIDER'S TIP
CHECK OUT THE NEW TAKE-OUT HATCH TWO DOORS DOWN

All-day brunch is a big deal here and sourdough, eggs and avo in various delicious combos are complemented by a black pudding stack with smoked back bacon, fried egg and cherry tomatoes. You'll also find creative lunch dishes such as the sharing platter of pork pie, ham, beef, cheese, bread and salad.

On the coffee front, Extract's wide range of beans provides all sorts of lip-smacking pairings on espresso, AeroPress and batch brew; the Dr Strangelove blend is a regular fave.

ESTABLISHED
2013

KEY ROASTER
Extract Coffee Roasters

BREWING METHODS
Espresso, AeroPress, batch brew

MACHINE
Sanremo Verona

GRINDER
Mahlkonig K30

OPENING HOURS
Mon-Sat
9am-5pm
Sun
9.30am-4pm

Gluten FREE

BEANS AVAILABLE
INSTORE

ALTERNATIVE MILK

WIFI

www.brewandbrownie.com   T: 01904 647420

f Brew & Brownie   🐦 @brewandbrownie   📷 @brewandbrownie

64. BURR COFFEE

5 Lendal, York, North Yorkshire, YO1 8AQ

Saints and sinners alike are drawn to this cosy York cafe which has been serving the local community for over a decade.

Coffee-loving angels find their beatific grins growing wider at the superfood salad bar with its fresh array of healthy options. Veggies and vegans rave about brunch faves such as herb marinated mushrooms on toast and American pancake stacks, while the handmade meat and vegetarian scotch egg salads are legendary.

INSIDER'S TIP CHECK OUT THE ARRAY OF LOCAL AND ARTISANAL BEERS AND CIDERS

Transgressors meanwhile, easily fall into temptation at the ever changing line-up of wicked bakes. Although chocolate peanut butter cake or gluten-free mini cups oozing with lemon curd, earl grey and white chocolate would bring out the devil in anyone.

Whether you're virtuous or gluttonous, the coffee offering at Burr is a universal rite. Leeds' North Star Coffee Roasters provides the main roast served as AeroPress, V60 or espresso, and if you're in a hurry both coffee and cuisine are available to-go.

ESTABLISHED
2006

KEY ROASTER
North Star
Coffee Roasters

BREWING METHODS
Espresso,
AeroPress, V60

MACHINE
Dalla Corte

GRINDERS
Mahlkonig K30,
Mahlkonig Vario

OPENING HOURS
Mon-Sat
8am-5pm
Sun 9am-4pm

Gluten FREE

BEANS AVAILABLE INSTORE

ALTERNATIVE MILK

CYCLE FRIENDLY

OUTDOOR SEATING

www.burrcoffee.co.uk   T: 01904 644410
f Burr   @burrcoffeeuk   @burrcoffee

65. SPRING ESPRESSO – LENDAL

21 Lendal, York, North Yorkshire, YO1 8AQ

If the original Spring Espresso on Fossgate is your go-to for weekend brunching, the new outpost in the city centre should be your mainstay for geeking out over the latest brews.

Launched in October 2016, the second speciality shop from UKBC sensory judge Steve Dyson and coffee-prenuer Tracey Peck, is home to the country's first Synesso Hydra MVP.

Doing the honours on the slick set-up is Square Mile's latest seasonal pick, while support in the second hopper comes courtesy of guest roaster Workshop.

INSIDER'S TIP LOOSE-LEAF LOVERS CAN GET STUCK INTO A HEFTY COLLECTION OF CANTON TEAS

A busy calendar of cupping and brewing events takes place after hours and welcomes all manner of enthusiasts who want to get stuck into Steve's latest finds and find out more about the mighty bean.

Like its sister cafe, a towering stack of pancakes or waffles laden with fresh fruit is the way to go when hunger hits. Though if you can see past the sweet sensations, the fresh, seasonal sandwiches and toasted panini are certainly no compromise.

ESTABLISHED
2016

KEY ROASTER
Square Mile
Coffee Roasters

BREWING METHODS
Espresso, V60,
AeroPress

MACHINE
Synesso Hydra
MVP

GRINDERS
Mythos One,
Mahlkonig EK 43

OPENING HOURS
Mon-Sun
8am-6pm

www.springespresso.co.uk   T: 01904 656556

f Spring Espresso   🐦 @springespresso   📷 @springespresso

MAP №66. THE ATTIC AND CAFE HARLEQUIN

2 King's Square, York, North Yorkshire, YO1 8BH

This dynamic coffee shop, with its multiple brewing methods and countless Has Bean single origins, will revive even the most jaded coffee palate.

Easy to locate on the main drag of the city's historic centre, the uninitiated make their way to the first floor cafe for traditional cream teas, savoury snacks, homemade treats and speciality coffee.

Those in the know, however, continue their climb to The Attic where, from Thursdays to Saturdays, the caffeine sorcery gets really geeky. Six different customised, single origin beans are available, each individually profiled for an optimum speciality experience.

INSIDER'S TIP CRAFT YOUR PERFECT G&T FROM ONE OF THE 70 DIFFERENT GINS IN THE ATTIC

You'll also find an eclectic mix of local artwork and a cracking gin line-up.

Doing nothing by halves, owner Gordon, a multi-disciplined national SCA champion and authorised trainer, also hosts brewing and barista masterclasses.

ESTABLISHED
2006

KEY ROASTER
Has Bean Coffee

BREWING METHODS
Espresso, EK shots, Kalita, V60, Clever Dripper, Chemex, french press, filter, AeroPress

MACHINES
Dalla Corte Mina x 2, Dalla Corte Evo 1

GRINDERS
Dalla Corte twin, Mythos One, Ditting 1203, Anfim Barista, Mahlkonig EK 43

OPENING HOURS
Cafe Harlequin:
Mon-Fri 10am-4pm
Sat 10am-5pm
Sun 10.30am-3.30pm
The Attic:
Thu-Sat 12pm-11pm

www.harlequinyork.com   T: 01904 630631

f The attic (at harlequins)   🐦 @harlequinyork   📷 @atticatharlequins

№67. THE FOSSGATE SOCIAL

25 Fossgate, York, North Yorkshire, YO1 9TA

Taking centre stage among the buzzing bars and restaurants of York's foodie quarter, Fossgate Social slides gleefully from daytime coffee shop to evening craft beer and cocktail venue, so you'll discover a cheerful welcome from breakfast to bedtime.

Start your day with a North Star flat white as you catch up on emails, stay on for lunch, then check out the extensive back bar for a boozy afternoon (and evening) in the courtyard. Espresso martinis are the aperitif of choice, and if you're lucky you may catch one of the open-mic nights, which showcase local talent.

INSIDER'S TIP
JOIN THE WEEKLY 5K FUN RUN UP AND DOWN THE RIVER

Don't want to drink in the evening? No drama: the coffee machine is fired up until late, or try the latest guest beans from Red Bank in a Chemex.

The team are enthusiastic about playing around with food and drink mash-ups so you can also get your thrills in the form of coffee porters and beer cake. It's just one of the homemade bakes for which the Social is loved, and which pull in the crowds for a slice of 'Social' life.

ESTABLISHED
2014

KEY ROASTER
North Star
Coffee Roasters

BREWING METHODS
Espresso,
Chemex

MACHINE
La Marzocco

GRINDERS
Mazzer x 2

OPENING HOURS
Mon-Thu
9am-12am
Fri-Sat
9am-12.30am
Sun
10am-12am

 Gluten FREE

 BEANS AVAILABLE INSTORE

 ALTE RNA TIVE MILK

 WIFI

---

www.thefossgatesocial.com T: 01904 628692

f the fossgate SOCIAL 🐦 @fossgatesocial 📷 @fossgatesocial

№68. SPRING ESPRESSO – FOSSGATE

45 Fossgate, York, North Yorkshire, YO1 9TF

One of the pioneers flying the flag for speciality in York, Spring Espresso was opened six years ago by UKBC sensory judge Steve Dyson and partner Tracey Peck, a former mobile coffee business owner.

Since then, the compact cafe has picked up a number of Beverage Standards Association awards, and been included in top coffee shop rankings by *The Times* and *The Independent*. The result is a loyal following of local coffee lovers and an almost constant queue for a table.

INSIDER'S TIP LOOK OUT FOR GUESTS SUCH AS LONDON'S WORKSHOP IN THE HOPPER

With an exclusively high-altitude seasonal coffee offering from Square Mile, you'd be forgiven for expecting a cluster of connoisseurs chatting coffee at the industrial style seats inside or on the wooden bench out front.

But with a first-class food bill covering all the brunch and lunch bases – the posh bacon sarnie and maple pecan pancake stack are particular faves – you'll discover folk at all levels of coffee experience tucking into good grub and flawless flat whites.

ESTABLISHED
2011

KEY ROASTER
Square Mile
Coffee Roasters

BREWING METHODS
Espresso, V60,
AeroPress

MACHINE
Synesso Hydra

GRINDER
Mythos One

OPENING HOURS
Mon-Sun
8am-6pm

www.springespresso.co.uk T: 07779 294149

f Spring Espresso 🐦 @springespresso 📷 @springespresso

ℳ.69. WESTMORELAND COFFEE

2 Westmoreland Street, Harrogate, North Yorkshire, HG1 5AT

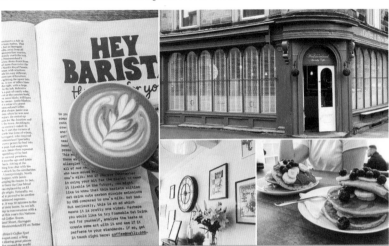

This slick cafe in suburban Harrogate has been popular for its impressive espresso and forward-thinking filters since Jamie Marlow set up shop in 2015.

'I first discovered speciality coffee as a student in the capital,' explains Jamie, *'although my passion for exploring coffee's flavour potential really flourished while I was living in New York and LA.'*

Starting with a small take-out espresso bar in 2014, the former Londoner soon realised he was going to need bigger digs to meet the demand for quality coffee, and took on a spacious plot just down the road.

INSIDER'S TIP: LET THE WAFT OF FRESHLY BAKED BROWNIES LEAD YOU TO WESTMORELAND'S DOOR

Westmoreland's North Star line-up has been joined by a diet-disgracing breakfast menu this year, which is stuffed with brunch faves such as buttermilk pancakes piled high with fresh fruit and maple syrup. Those wanting to reign in the indulgence can forgo any food FOMO with golden granola-layered greek yogurt and fruit, or chunky avo and poached eggs with locally baked sourdough.

ESTABLISHED
2014

KEY ROASTER
North Star Coffee Roasters

BREWING METHODS
Espresso, AeroPress, cold brew, pourover

MACHINE
La Spaziale

GRINDER
Sanremo

OPENING HOURS
Mon-Fri 8.30am-5pm
Sat 9am-3pm

www.westmorelandcoffee.com T: 01423 562918

f WestmorelandSpecialityCoffee 🐦 @westmorelandCFE 📷 @thecoffeebarharrogate

MAP 70. BEAN & BUD

14 Commercial Street, Harrogate, North Yorkshire, HG1 1TY

Photos: Ideal Imagery

While the burgeoning selection of beans, serve styles and coffee kit at this Harrogate hangout could spook the speciality newbie, coffee snobbery is something co-founders Ruth Hampson and Hayden Howells have always been keen to nip in the bud.

INSIDER'S TIP THE SPECIALITY TEAS ARE AWARD WINNING. TRY A CHINESE OOLONG OR A JAPANESE SENCHA

'We wanted to create an informative but friendly space where everyone can try the very best beans without feeling confused or overwhelmed,' explains Ruth. 'So we're keen to share knowledge without being pretentious or preachy.'

You'll find a crack team of clued-up baristas behind the bar, happy to dish out top-notch advice on the roster of roasts available. The two espressos and two slow-brewed filters change every two weeks to showcase the spectrum of flavours the coffee plant offers, and guests such as London's Caravan make appearances on the brew bar.

Bean & Bud is also launching an online shop, so that home enthusiasts can get speciality beans, loose-leaf teas and brewing accessories delivered to their door.

ESTABLISHED
2010

KEY ROASTERS
Round Hill Roastery, Campbell & Syme, Pharmacie

BREWING METHODS
Espresso, Kalita Wave, V60, AeroPress, Chemex

MACHINE
La Marzocco Strada EP

GRINDERS
Mythos x 2, Mahlkonig K30, Mahlkonig Tanzania

OPENING HOURS
Mon-Sat 8am-5pm
Sun 10am-4pm

Gluten FREE · BEANS AVAILABLE INSTORE · ALTERNATIVE MILK · WIFI · OUTDOOR SEATING · DISABLED ACCESS · COFFEE COURSES

www.beanandbud.co.uk T: 01423 508200
f Bean & Bud 🐦 @beanandbud 📷 @beanandbud

MAP 71. STARLING INDEPENDENT BEER & COFFEE HOUSE

47 Oxford Street, Harrogate, North Yorkshire, HG1 1PW

Pop into Starling for a morning brew and you could easily end up staying until bedtime. After all, the coffee machine is dialled in and ready for action until 11pm at this spacious Harrogate haunt.

Alongside espresso roasted by Yorkshire's Dark Woods, you'll find three or four single origins on V60 and a single estate Guatemalan decaf espresso (ground to order).

INSIDER'S TIP FEELING NAUGHTY? TRY THE DARK WOODS ESPRESSO MARTINI

Add a phenomenal selection of craft beers, a mean gin shelf and regular live music nights and you could easily lose a day at this eatery-bar-coffee-house which extends over several floors. On the food front, handcrafted Neapolitan pizzas are the big draw, especially with slow cooked pulled pork, or flipped into a chicken and chorizo calzone.

Be sure to check out the Bonzer brunch menu and selection of cakes. And don't miss the quirky chip combos such as poutine: fries topped with homemade gravy and Yorkshire cheese curd (yep, really).

ESTABLISHED
2017

KEY ROASTER
Dark Woods Coffee

BREWING METHODS
Espresso, V60

MACHINE
La Marzocco Linea

GRINDERS
Mahlkonig EK 43, Mazzer Super Jolly

OPENING HOURS
Mon-Sat
9am-11pm
Mon-Sat
9am-10.30pm

Gluten FREE

BEANS AVAILABLE INSTORE

ALTERNATIVE MILK

WIFI

FAMILY FRIENDLY

www.starlinghgte.co.uk T: 01423 531310

f Starling Independent Beer & Coffee House 🐦 @starlinghgte 📷 @starlinghgte

> HOUSE OF KOKO №81

72. HOXTON NORTH

1 Royal Parade, Harrogate, North Yorkshire, HG1 2SZ

Queen Victoria would certainly have approved of Hoxton North. For one, it's located on the Royal Parade which 170 years ago, housed the kings and queens of Europe who visited to take the restorative waters of Harrogate's Pump Rooms.

And of course, Queen Vic was a great foodie who enthusiastically embraced breakfast, so we're pretty sure she would have found these epic brunches agreeable.

But nowadays, it's Hoxton North's reputation for remarkable coffee that attracts customers. Named after the East End district renowned for its independent coffee shop culture, founders Timothy and Victoria Bosworth wanted their hip bar to be an oasis of specialist coffee.

INSIDER'S TIP
QUIZ THE GANG ON THE LATEST GIN RESIDENCY

Consequently, the drinks offering is as fresh as the cool decor, with the Origin house roast supplemented by regularly changing guests.

Buzzing from dawn 'til dusk, Hoxton North turns into a bar from midday, serving still and sparkling wines, craft beers and spirits.

ESTABLISHED
2013

KEY ROASTER
Origin Coffee Roasters

BREWING METHOD
Espresso

MACHINE
La Marzocco Linea PB

GRINDER
Victoria Arduino Mythos One

OPENING HOURS
Mon-Thu
8.30am-9pm
Fri 8.30am-11pm
Sat 9.30am-11pm
Sun 10am-5pm

 Gluten FREE
 BEANS AVAILABLE INSTORE
 ALTERNATIVE MILK
 WIFI
 OUTDOOR seating
 FAMILY FRIENDLY

www.hoxtonnorth.com T: 01423 564061
f Hoxton North @hoxtonnorth @hoxtonnorth

MAP 73. THE HEDGEROW

Station Road, Threshfield, Near Skipton, North Yorkshire, BD23 5BP

If, on your first visit to The Hedgerow, you're a little confused as to why you appear to be in a florist shop, take a second sniff.

For beneath the woody foliage notes and scented floral bouquets, you'll nose out the welcoming waft of coffee on the breeze.

INSIDER'S TIP PICK UP A BUNCH OF BLOOMS FOR YOUR MAIN SQUEEZE WHILE GETTING A FLAT WHITE FIX

That'll be the doing of Heather, the daughter of green-fingered Wendy Hutchinson, who has recently honed her skills at the legendary Barn roastery in Berlin. After a stint working on an organic farm in Portugal three years ago, Heather decided to join her mum in the family business.

Together with their amazing team, they reworked the concept to cover both blooms and beans, and refurbished the space to include an open plan kitchen and indoor seating, along with creating a little piece of paradise in the suntrap courtyard.

A hidden speciality coffee find in the Dales, The Hedgerow has become a one-stop destination for flowers, crumpets, cakes and that all-important caffeine fix.

ESTABLISHED
1993

KEY ROASTER
Atkinsons

BREWING METHODS
Espresso, filter

MACHINE
Nuova Simonelli

GRINDER
Mythos

OPENING HOURS
Tue-Fri
9am-5pm
Sat 9am-4pm

Gluten FREE

BEANS AVAILABLE INSTORE

ALTERNATIVE MILK

WIFI

CYCLE FRIENDLY

OUTDOOR seating

FAMILY friendly

DISABLED ACCESS

BRING YOUR OWN Cup

COFFEE COURSES

---

www.the-hedgerow.co.uk T: 01756 752293
f The Hedgerow, Threshfield @the-hedgerow

MAP 74. LAY OF THE LAND CAFE

Kings Mill Lane, Settle, North Yorkshire, BD24 9BS

Forget any disparaging ideas you may hold about garden centre cafes; this one is run by a former chef who trained at Michelin starred Northcote hotel in Langho, and who serves small batch roasted speciality coffee.

Modernist and stylish in a white tiled, industrial lighting, reclaimed wood sort of way, James Lay's joint is an oasis of good coffee and grub in Settle, right in the heart of the Yorkshire Dales.

Coffee comes courtesy of Casa Espresso which is served as espresso, AeroPress and pourover. *'We usually only have one type of coffee on at any time, but we try to stick to single origin and change the coffee every month if we can,'* says James.

INSIDER'S TIP COFFEE IS SERVED IN APPROPRIATE 'GET EXCITED AND GROW THINGS' MUGS

As you'd imagine, he goes big on the grub and has created a constantly evolving lunch and breakfast menu with sandwiches, soups and hot and cold meals all made to order.

Freshly baked cakes, including an *'awesome gluten-free chocolate brownie'* and scones hit the spot with the sweet-toothed.

ESTABLISHED
2015

KEY ROASTER
Casa Espresso

BREWING METHODS
Espresso,
AeroPress,
pourover

MACHINE
Sanremo Verona

GRINDER
Sanremo SR70 EVO

OPENING HOURS
Mon-Sat
9am-4.30pm
Sun 10am-3pm

www.layoftheland.co.uk T: 01729 824247
Lay of the Land - Garden Centre & Cafe @lay_of_the_land @layoftheland_settle

MAP 75. BEAN LOVED COFFEE BAR

17 Otley Street, Skipton, North Yorkshire, BD23 1DY

Flying the flag for indie and local in Skipton for a decade, Bean Loved is the kind of coffee bar every town deserves.

Serious about speciality, it has held Beverage Standards Association four cup accreditation for the last three years, and owner Wes and family work closely with the excellent Dark Woods in the creation of Bean Loved's house espresso.

Eschewing multiple serve styles and a brew bar in favour of excelling in espresso, choice comes in the form of additional guest roasts from the likes of Square Mile and Workshop.

INSIDER'S TIP BUY THE BEAN LOVED BLEND TO TAKE AWAY

There are also plenty of top picks on the food menu. Breakfast, brunch and lunch are all covered by the in-house chefs who collaborate with local producers to create pop up events at the cafe, as well as menus.

Passion is the golden thread that runs through everything and Wes says, *'It's what built our reputation and helped us reach new audiences in Skipton.'*

ESTABLISHED
2007

KEY ROASTER
Dark Woods Coffee

BREWING METHOD
Espresso

MACHINE
La Marzocco FB80

GRINDERS
Nuova Simonelli Mythos One, Mahlkonig EK 43

OPENING HOURS
Mon-Fri
7.30am-5pm
Sat 8am-5pm
Sun 9am-5pm

Gluten FREE

BEANS AVAILABLE
INSTORE

ALTERNATIVE MILK

WIFI

CYCLE FRIENDLY

OUTDOOR seating

FAMILY friendly

DISABLED ACCESS

BRING YOUR OWN Cup

www.beanloved.co.uk T: 01756 791534

f Bean Loved 🐦 @beanloved 📷 @beanloved

76. THE COMMUTE CYCLE CAFE

20 Leeds, Road, Ilkley, West Yorkshire, LS29 8DS

A proper ploughman's and smooth Origin espresso isn't what you'd expect to find when taking your bike for a quick tune up. But at this multifaceted mash-up, top-notch brews and local fodder receive the same care as the cycles.

A family run business, the popular hangout is fuelled by both passion and the cycling obsession which, post-Tour de Yorkshire, has exploded in Ilkley.

Fresh from exploring the surrounding countryside, mountain bikers, road cyclists and ramblers flock to The Commute for its friendly vibe, daily filter specials and locally sourced fare.

INSIDER'S TIP CHECK OUT THE EVENTS CALENDAR FOR A TASTE OF ILKLEY ACTIVITY

Soothe sore limbs with an expertly pulled espresso, or linger over something special on AeroPress. There's a real community spirit here, so don't be afraid to ask the baristas for their latest pick of the guest roasts.

ESTABLISHED
2016

KEY ROASTER
Origin
Coffee Roasters

BREWING METHODS
Espresso, filter,
AeroPress

MACHINE
La Marzocco
Linea PB

GRINDERS
Mythos x 2

OPENING HOURS
Mon-Wed
8am-4pm
Fri 8am-4pm
Sat 8.30am-5pm
Sun 8am-4pm

 Gluten FREE

 BEANS AVAILABLE INSTORE

 ALTE RNA TIVE MILK

 WIFI

 CYCLE FRIENDLY

 OUTDOOR seating

 FAMILY friendly

 BRING YOUR OWN cup.

 COFFEE COURSES

www.thecommuteyorkshire.com T: 07888 942007

f The Commute Coffee House and Cycle-Workshop 🐦 @uthecommuteyorks 📷 @thecommutecyclecafe

77. SALAMI & CO.

10 Market Place, Otley, West Yorkshire, LS21 3AQ

Dog-loving husband and wife team, Simon and Lucy, are the duo behind Salami & Co. – a coffee house that proudly caters for both human and hound.

Named after Salami the dachshund, this cafe isn't simply accommodating of dogs; it goes so far as to provide dog beds, towels, water bowls and a separate canine menu.

INSIDER'S TIP
TRY THE AMAZING VARIETY OF CAKES: LAVENDER, ELDERFLOWER, ROSE AND RASPBERRY FRANGIPANE

While your dog is having its day, bean purists will revel in the care poured into every cup: beans are carefully sourced to fit the intended brew method, whether espresso, V60 or cold brew.

Salami & Co. has also welcomed nitro to the brew party, which has proved popular for its silky texture and rich, buttery flavours.

An accompanying menu of healthy and hearty options is more than equal to anything the pooches receive, and it's all freshly prepared on site with local ingredients.

ESTABLISHED
2016

KEY ROASTERS
Casa Espresso, Maude Coffee Roasters

BREWING METHODS
Espresso, V60, nitro, cold brew

MACHINE
Sanremo Verona RS

GRINDER
Sanremo

OPENING HOURS
Mon-Thu
8am-6pm
Fri-Sat 8am-8pm
Sun 8am-4.30pm

 Gluten FREE

 BEANS AVAILABLE / INSTORE

 ALTERNATIVE MILK

 WIFI

www.salamiandco.com T: 01943 968207

f Salami & Co 🐦 @salamiandco 📷 @salamiandco

MAP № 78. BLOOMFIELD SQUARE

28-30 Gay Lane, Otley, Leeds, West Yorkshire, LS21 1BR

If there was a definitive ranking of smells at *Indy Coffee Guide* HQ, the whiff of fresh print and waft of brewing coffee would definitely tussle for the top spot.

It's a sensory conundrum shared by Tony Wright and Emma Thorpe, whose charming Otley cafe sees the euphoric scents collide under one creative roof.

With a La Marzocco out front and a Victorian printing press out back, it's a sure bet that there aren't many speciality shops that can offer a schooling in letterpress printing alongside a locally roasted North Star espresso and homemade hunk of flapjack.

INSIDER'S TIP COUNTER YOUR CAFFEINE LEVELS WITH BARISTA ELLIOTT'S RHUBARB TONIC

Lessons don't stop at A to Z though; there's a timetable of caffeine events where you can brush up on your home brewing while you sample Tony and Emma's latest pick of coffees via the V60 and AeroPress.

The sweet selection of vinyl, eclectic decor and all-round chilled vibes have been expertly curated by a couple of creatives: Tony is lead singer with UK rock band Terrorvision while co-owner and girlfriend Emma is the cafe's visionary interior designer.

ESTABLISHED
2016

KEY ROASTER
North Star
Coffee Roasters

BREWING METHODS
Espresso, V60,
AeroPress

MACHINE
La Marzocco
Linear PB AV

GRINDERS
Mahlkonig K30
Air, Mazzer Luigi

OPENING HOURS
Tue-Sat
9am-5pm
Sun 10am-4pm

Gluten FREE

BEANS AVAILABLE / INSTORE

ALTERNATIVE MILK

WIFI

CYCLE FRIENDLY

OUTDOOR seating

FAMILY friendly

DISABLED ACCESS

COFFEE COURSES

---

www.bloomfieldsquare.co.uk T: 01943 463683

f Bloomfield Square 🐦 @bloomfieldsqr ⚪ @bloomfield_square

MAP 79. TAMBOURINE COFFEE

38 Bingley Road, Saltaire, Bradford, West Yorkshire, BD18 4RU

Fed up with clocking up miles just to get a decent coffee, Chris Large decided it was time to roll up his sleeves and set up shop himself – well, someone had to do it.

Armed with bags of enthusiasm and seven years' experience developing his skills at speciality coffee shop Out of the Woods, Chris opened the doors of Tambourine in the heart of the Victorian World Heritage Site of Saltaire.

INSIDER'S TIP CHECK OUT THE GUEST ROASTS AND ARTWORK WHICH BOTH CHANGE MONTHLY

Whether you opt for an artfully-crafted espresso based drink or a pourover, you're in safe hands. '*I work with North Star for my resident espresso beans, but also offer an ever-changing choice of single origin coffees from guest roasters*,' says Chris. If you want to learn from the master himself, make a note of the regular coffee tastings and evening events.

While you're savouring your brew, there's plenty to keep kids out of mischief, with a stack of books and blackboards to play with. And if they scream for ice cream, you can relax in the knowledge that Northern Bloc's lovely range of flavours are waiting in the freezer.

ESTABLISHED
2017

KEY ROASTER
North Star
Coffee Roasters

BREWING METHODS
Espresso, V60,
cold brew

MACHINE
Sanremo Verona

GRINDERS
Mahlkonig K30,
Sanremo

OPENING HOURS
Mon-Fri
7.30am-5pm
Sat 8.30am-5pm
Sun 10am-4pm

www.tambourinecoffee.co.uk T: 01274 945870

🐦 @tambourinecoffe 📷 @tambourinecoffee

MAP 80. BOWERY

54 Otley Road, Headingley, Leeds, West Yorkshire, LS6 2AL

To get a true flavour of Bowery in Headingley, you need to spend an afternoon immersed in its creative environment.

From the hearty greeting of owners Ged and Sandra Togher to the perfectly smooth Allpress Redchurch espresso, it's a pleasurable, inspiring space in which to while away a few hours.

INSIDER'S TIP TRY THE LEGENDARY TOASTED CHEESE SCONE WITH CITRUS AND CARROT JAM

Now entering its 10th year, the well established coffee destination doubles up as a micro-gallery, showcasing a wide range of contemporary visual art. Local creatives also provide gifts and artwork which is on sale.

There's a busy schedule of short courses and events, as well as regular coffee workshops with Ged, where budding baristas can learn the tricks of the trade to improve their coffee making at home.

In addition, a busy little kitchen crafts seasonal soups, salads and lunch plates, along with much-loved bakes such as banana and walnut loaf.

ESTABLISHED
2008

KEY ROASTER
Allpress Espresso

BREWING METHOD
Espresso

MACHINE
CMA Astoria

GRINDER
Mazzer Super Jolly

OPENING HOURS
Mon-Thu
8.30am-6.30pm
Fri-Sat
8.30am-6pm
Sun 10am-5pm

 Gluten FREE

 BEANS AVAILABLE INSTORE

 ALTERNATIVE MILK

 WIFI

 CYCLE FRIENDLY

OUTDOOR SEATING

 FAMILY FRIENDLY

COFFEE COURSES

www.thebowery.org   T: 01132 242284

f Bowery   🐦 @theboweryarts   📷 @boweryleeds

MAP№ 81. HOUSE OF KOKO

62 Harrogate Road, Chapel Allerton, Leeds, West Yorkshire, LS7 4LA

A pleasing balance of clean lines and kitsch touches creates a home-from-home vibe at this light and airy space. So you'll feel suitably comfy sinking a locally roasted North Star coffee with your sourdough toastie while nattering with the throng of regulars who congregate at this Chapel Allerton community hub.

In addition to cracking coffee, it's the baked goods – including plenty of veggie and vegan offerings – that are the house speciality.

And if you can handle the FOMO, check out House of Koko's Instagram page for the latest batch before you make a trip.

INSIDER'S TIP
CHECK OUT THE VEGAN WEDNESDAYS AND GLUTEN-FREE FRIDAY CAKE SPECIALS

Swing by when the sun is shining, as the outdoor space gets all-day rays and is a great people watching perch with a Fitch cold brew to hand.

Come the weekend, this spot is usually heaving with students, families and coffee geeks all sampling the latest guest roasts and brunching on stacks of fluffy pancakes and avo smothered sourdough. Follow the crowd.

ESTABLISHED
2015

KEY ROASTER
North Star Coffee Roasters

BREWING METHODS
Espresso, drip

MACHINE
Astoria Gloria AL3

GRINDERS
Anfim, Mazzer

OPENING HOURS
Mon-Fri 8am-5pm
Sat 9am-5pm
Sun 10am-4pm

 Gluten FREE

 BEANS AVAILABLE INSTORE

 ALTERNATIVE MILK

 WIFI

 CYCLE FRIENDLY

 OUTDOOR SEATING

 FAMILY FRIENDLY

 DISABLED ACCESS

 BRING YOUR OWN CUP

www.houseofkoko.com T: 01132 621808

f House of Koko 🐦 @houseofkoko 📷 @houseofkoko

№82. STAGE ESPRESSO & BREWBAR

41 Great George Street, Leeds, West Yorkshire, LS1 3BB

Sandwiched between Leeds' iconic General Infirmary and the Town Hall, two inspirational brothers (and their beagle Copper) have created a fresh, Nordic-inspired cafe.

Using Union coffee, Matt and Martyn Jakeman – who are hot on coffee quality and sustainability – provide a superb choice of brew methods including single origin espresso as well as Kalita Wave, Clever Dripper and batch filter brews.

INSIDER'S TIP: ORDER THE BATCH BREW, THEN SEEK OUT COPPER FOR A CUDDLE

Another recent addition is the downstairs seating area, which is a great pit-stop for office-types, students and shoppers, with weekly foodie specials tempting visitors to stay beyond a quick cup.

A host of events and evening happenings are also on the cards and promises to provide a pleasing mash-up of the city's caffeine culture with local bands, artists and creatives.

ESTABLISHED
2017

KEY ROASTER
Union Hand-Roasted Coffee

BREWING METHODS
Espresso, Kalita Wave, Clever Dripper, batch brew

MACHINE
La Marzocco Linea Classic

GRINDERS
Mythos One, Mahlkonig EK 43

OPENING HOURS
Mon-Fri
8am-5pm
Sat 9am-5pm

Gluten FREE

BEANS AVAILABLE INSTORE

ALTERNATIVE MILK

WIFI

---

www.stagecoffee.com T: 07527 534983

f Stage Espresso & Brewbar 🐦 @stagecoffee 📷 @stagecoffeeleeds

MAP 83. LA BOTTEGA MILANESE – THE LIGHT

The Headrow, Leeds, West Yorkshire, LS1 8TL

The original in the La Bottega legacy, this Leeds coffee institution opened in 2009 – way before speciality went mainstream. Set in the heart of The Light centre, LBM mixes traditional Milanese dining with a focus on the third wave.

It's the same European cafe culture concept that you'll find at its big sister down the road, and longer opening hours make it a great spot for post-shopping caffeine hits and pre-cinema drinkies.

INSIDER'S TIP
PICK UP A BAG OF THE LBM BLEND TO SAVOUR AT HOME

Enjoy a custom blend espresso (a collaboration with Dark Woods in Marsden) or one of the rotating guest single origins from a roster of quality roasters.

Amid the city's growing coffee scene, La Bottega Milanese is one of the pioneers of speciality. And true to owner Alex's Italian roots, the team's attention is firmly on customer care and the creation of a perfect coffee experience.

In a city centre spot you may expect the community vibe to be lacking, but not here. It's like a little slice of Italy, served up in an immaculately fresh and inviting setting.

ESTABLISHED
2009

KEY ROASTER
Dark Woods Coffee

BREWING METHODS
Espresso, batch brew

MACHINE
Faema E61 Legend

GRINDER
Mythos

OPENING HOURS
Mon-Thu
7.30am-8pm
Fri 7.30am-9pm
Sat 9am-9pm
Sun 10am-7pm

BEANS AVAILABLE INSTORE

ALTERNATIVE MILK

WIFI

OUTDOOR Seating

DISABLED ACCESS

BRING YOUR OWN Cup

www.labottegamilanese.co.uk   T: 01132 454242

f La Bottega Milanese   🐦 @bottegamilanese   📷 @labottegamilanese

84. KAPOW COFFEE

15 Thornton's Arcade, Leeds, West Yorkshire, LS1 6LQ

Kapow's second venture in the city, this three-floor, retro joint at the heart of Leeds' Thornton's Arcade is the antithesis of copycat cafe interior design.

Arty pictures and photos, coffee magazines and books make it a fun and relaxing space in which to kick back and enjoy a quality brew. The neon Kapow sign in the window says it all: whether you're after a morning jolt or an afternoon caffeine fix, a fantastic coffee hit awaits inside.

If you're in a rush, the house espresso blend from Union is a quality hit to-go, while luscious shakes and a haul of herbal teas are also on hand.

INSIDER'S TIP LOOK OUT FOR FUTURE EXHIBITIONS BY ARTISTS AND PHOTOGRAPHERS

Alternatively, try something from the selection of guest blends – Colonna, North Star and Dark Woods – as espresso or V60.

And treats like honeycomb rocky road and millionaire's shortbread at the counter provide a satisfying accompanying sugar high.

ESTABLISHED
2013

KEY ROASTER
Union Hand-Roasted Coffee

BREWING METHODS
Espresso, V60

MACHINE
Sanremo

GRINDER
Mazzer

OPENING HOURS
Mon-Sat
8am-6pm
Sun 10am-5pm

BEANS AVAILABLE
INSTORE

ALTERNATIVE MILK

WIFI

OUTDOOR seating

MAP № 85. LA BOTTEGA MILANESE – BOND COURT

2 Bond Court, Leeds, West Yorkshire, LS1 2JZ

With Italian Alex Galantino at the helm, La Bottega's Milanese influences – modern architecture, cafe culture and attention to detail – are a delicious mix. Such is the level of care throughout, it's little wonder that the team was asked to do the honours at Harvey Nichols' cafe last Christmas.

Old-school southern European charm meets new wave coffee at this fusion cafe, where an early morning brew sipped at the window bench slowly morphs to early evening aperitivos at the cluster of tables.

INSIDER'S TIP VISIT LATE AFTERNOON FOR A POST-WORK ESPRESSO AND APEROL SPRITZ

La Bottega sets the bar high on its meticulous mission: pastries are sourced from Italy while down-the-road roasted coffee from Dark Woods is crafted exclusively for the cafe in consultation with the La Bottega crew.

'Our team and customers pick the beans, select the roast profile and vote on a shortlist of three coffees,' says Alex. *'Then our barista visits Dark Woods to help with the roast.'*

So much more than a pit-stop for a caffeine hit, make like an Italian and take time to feast on fabulous food while chewing the fat with fellow coffee aficionados.

ESTABLISHED
2009

KEY ROASTER
Dark Woods Coffee

BREWING METHODS
Espresso, batch brew, V60, AeroPress

MACHINE
Kees van der WestenMirage

GRINDER
Mythos

OPENING HOURS
Mon-Tue 7am-6pm
Wed-Thu 7am-7pm
Fri 7am-9pm
Sat 9am-9pm
Sun 10am-6pm

BEANS AVAILABLE INSTORE

ALTERNATIVE MILK

WIFI

CYCLE FRIENDLY

OUTDOOR SEATING

DISABLED ACCESS

BRING YOUR OWN CUP

www.labottegamilanese.co.uk   T: 01132 431102

f La Bottega Milanese   🐦 @bottegamilanese   📷 @labottegamilanese

MAP 86. LAYNES ESPRESSO

16 New Station Street, Leeds, West Yorkshire, LS1 5DL

Scoring a table at this institution took stealth and exquisite timing before its recent expansion. Knocking through into the neighbouring building, the former espresso bar has gone from 15 to 55 seats, while the food and coffee offering has been elevated from grab-and-go to swig-and-savour.

A new open-plan kitchen has broken the brunch boundaries, introducing dishes such as the Laynes Breakfast: a twist on the full English with homemade braised beans, roasted shallots, chestnut and lemon patty and Mayfield cheese.

INSIDER'S TIP THE TALENTED TEAM OFFER A COMPREHENSIVE COLLECTION OF COFFEE COURSES

Always on the lookout for exciting beans, owner Dave Olejnik curates an eclectic collection of international guest roasters – recent residencies include Drop, Round Hill and Per Nordby – alongside Laynes' mainstay, Square Mile.

Try the split shot – a piccolo with a single espresso on the side – paired with a brioche bostock from a local French bakery, or an incredibly fancy cherry bakewell, crafted exclusively for Laynes.

ESTABLISHED
2011

KEY ROASTER
Square Mile
Coffee Roasters

BREWING METHODS
Espresso, V60,
AeroPress

MACHINE
Synesso MVP

GRINDER
Mythos

OPENING HOURS
Mon-Fri
7am-7pm
Sat-Sun
9am-6pm

 Gluten FREE

 BEANS AVAILABLE INSTORE

 ALTERNATIVE MILK

 WIFI

 FAMILY FRIENDLY

www.laynesespresso.co.uk   T: 07828 823189

f Laynes Espresso   🐦 @laynesespresso   📷 @laynesespresso

MAP 87. OUT OF THE WOODS – GRANARY WHARF

Watermans Place, Granary Wharf, Leeds, West Yorkshire, LS1 4GL

This light and airy forest-themed nook sits quietly amid the bustle of the city. Just a coffee bean's throw from the main train station, it's somewhere for a quiet moment: think log cabin with better coffee.

Out of the Woods serves, appropriately, Dark Woods espresso, alongside traditional Yorkshire Tea and locally sourced brownies, breads and everything in between; it's no surprise it's featured in *The Leeds and West Yorkshire Cook Book*.

The coffee's really good (espresso-based only), but shies away from coffee snobbery. Manager Laura says: *'This is no hipster-only joint. This is proper coffee without the attitude'*. It echoes founder Ross's commitment to making quality drinks accessible to all, be they coffee connoisseur or novice.

INSIDER'S TIP
PLAY 'SPOT THE SQUIRREL' AT THE WOODLAND-THEMED CAFE

With the canal in sight, indoor and outdoor seating offers an all-year-round chill-out zone. Loyal regulars drop in mid dog walk, office workers hold informal catch ups and exhausted travellers relax with a proper coffee in this coppice of calm.

ESTABLISHED
2010

KEY ROASTER
Dark Woods Coffee

BREWING METHOD
Espresso

MACHINE
La Spaziale

GRINDER
Mahlkonig K30

OPENING HOURS
Mon-Fri
7am-4pm
Sat
8.30am-4pm

 Gluten FREE

 BEANS AVAILABLE INSTORE

 ALTERNATIVE MILK

 WIFI

CYCLE FRIENDLY

OUTDOOR SEATING

  DISABLED ACCESS

www.outofthewoods.me.uk T: 01132 454144
 Out of the Woods @outofthewoodsuk @outofthewoodsuk

MAP 88. OUT OF THE WOODS – WATER LANE

113 Water Lane, Leeds, West Yorkshire, LS11 5WD

Small and perfectly formed, this lovely little cafe which was opened over a decade ago by Ross Halliday, puts coffee as high on the agenda as the sandwiches, soups and hearty salads made with locally sourced and organic ingredients.

The coffee has local credentials too, via the excellent Dark Woods in Marsden, while tea has been carefully chosen from Tea Pigs and Yorkshire Tea.

As a result of all this care, Ross' little oasis of good things has long been a popular breakfast, brunch and lunchtime haunt for lucky locals and those working in the hipster industrial work spaces surrounding the cafe.

INSIDER'S TIP DRINK YOUR LOCALLY ROASTED ESPRESSO WITH LOCAL, ORGANIC MILK

Much like its younger sister in the canal basin of Granary Wharf, a visit here is a rejuvenating experience in the woods – but without any mud and with a lot more cake.

And if you don't feel all gooey inside from the warm welcome from Ross and her crew, one of the sinful salted caramel brownies from local artisan bakery, Brown & Blonde, should do the trick.

ESTABLISHED
2006

KEY ROASTER
Dark Woods Coffee

BREWING METHOD
Espresso

MACHINE
Delatte

GRINDER
Mahlkonig K30

OPENING HOURS
Mon-Fri
7am-4pm

 Gluten FREE

 BEANS AVAILABLE INSTORE

 ALTE RNA TIVE MILK

 WIFI

 CYCLE FRIENDLY

 DISABLED ACCESS

 BRING YOUR OWN Cup

www.outofthewoods.me.uk   T: 01132 448123
f Out of the Woods   🐦 @outofthewoodsuk   📷 @outofthewoodsuk

89. THE GRUB & GROG SHOP

3 Sheaf Street, Leeds, West Yorkshire, LS10 1HD

A mere hop, skip and a jump from the city centre, The Grub & Grog Shop is a coffee destination worth seeking out.

Occupying Sheaf Street Cafeteria alongside Duke Studios, the sociable hub fuels fans with coffee that's roasted just along the canal at North Star's new digs.

Vegans and veggies are well catered for on a brunch menu brimming with colourful treats, while organic meat and free-range eggs feature throughout the homemade fodder.

INSIDER'S TIP: CALL IN FOR COFFEE; STAY FOR TABLE TENNIS

The team lives by the motto 'slow down', so take time over your speciality brew or the local-brewery-based bar menu and make the most of free table tennis in the suntrap courtyard when it's warm.

The delights are also available to take away, along with coffee to-go, beans, ground coffee and a range of filter gear.

ESTABLISHED
2016

KEY ROASTER
North Star
Coffee Roasters

BREWING METHOD
Espresso

MACHINE
La Marzocco
Linea Classic

GRINDER
Mazzer

OPENING HOURS
Mon-Thu
8.30am-5pm
Fri 8.30am-9pm
Sat 9am-9pm
Sun 9am-4pm

Gluten FREE

BEANS AVAILABLE INSTORE

ALTERNATIVE MILK

WIFI

CYCLE FRIENDLY

OUTDOOR seating

FAMILY friendly

DISABLED ACCESS

BRING YOUR OWN Cup

www.grubandgrog.co.uk T: 07513 492174
f The Grub & Grog Shop 🐦 @grubandgrogshop 📷 @grubandgrog

MAP 90. COFFEEVOLUTION

8 Church Street, Huddersfield, West Yorkshire, HD1 1DD

Huddersfield may not host as vibrant a speciality scene as some of its northern neighbours, yet visitors to the market town can find seriously accomplished coffee here thanks to one of the region's coffee pioneers.

Setting up his corner cafe before most baristas had even heard of a flat white, owner Jeremy Perkins was a professional viola player before his career switch to speciality in 2000.

INSIDER'S TIP CHECK OUT THE ART, MUSIC AND THEATRE EVENTS

Seventeen years later, he's still pouring his passion into coffee and stocking Coffeevolution with beauties from Bean Brothers, his roasting collaboration with brother James.

The bros' beans can be experienced in a sweeping selection of brew styles including AeroPress and Chemex, along with nitro cold brew and a house coffee stout. Round Hill and Atkinsons feature among other guests.

Grab a pew at one of the benches by the floor-to-ceiling windows and refuel with a pick from the fantastic foodie offering: panini, salads and grilled cheese sarnies join a cracking cohort of cakes baked by sister, Sally.

ESTABLISHED
2000

KEY ROASTER
Bean Brothers
Coffee Company

BREWING METHODS
Espresso, V60,
Chemex,
AeroPress,
cold brew, nitro

MACHINE
La Marzocco
FB80

GRINDERS
Mazzer Kony,
Mazzer Royal

OPENING HOURS
Mon-Fri
7am-7pm
Sat 7.30am-7pm
Sun 9am-6pm

 Gluten FREE

 BEANS AVAILABLE / INSTORE

 ALTERNATIVE MILK

 WIFI

 CYCLE FRIENDLY

 OUTDOOR Seating

 FAMILY FRIENDLY

 DISABLED ACCESS

 BRING YOUR OWN CUP

COFFEE COURSES

---

www.coffeevolution.co.uk   T: 01484 432881

f Coffeevolution Huddersfield   🐦 @coffeevolution   📷 @coffeevolutionhuddersfield

MAP № 91. ESPRESSO CORNER

11 Kirkgate, Huddersfield, West Yorkshire, HD1 1QS

Hit this popular spot on the corner of Wood Street at rush hour and you'll join a throng of Huddersfieldians swooning over silky espresso and slices of sweet treats.

Locals flock to the light-flooded coffee shop for the Under Milk Wood cappuccinos: a syrupy coffee with caramel flavours from Dark Woods, that's best imbibed with milk.

Square Mile's seasonal Red Brick also makes an appearance in the hopper, flaunting creamy notes of hazelnut, banoffee and apricot.

INSIDER'S TIP DON'T THINK ABOUT LEAVING WITHOUT DEVOURING A SLICE OF HOMEMADE MILLIONAIRE'S SHORTBREAD

Yorkshire-baked cakes and pastries are the perfect pairing to your pick of the poison, and freshly crafted sandwiches – chunky chicken, avo and smoked bacon on handcut artisan bread, yum – make sticking around for lunch an enticing invitation.

There's plenty of space for lingerers too, as old school desks – complete with original graffiti – line the room.

ESTABLISHED
2013

KEY ROASTER
Square Mile
Coffee Roasters

BREWING METHODS
Espresso, V60,
AeroPress

MACHINE
La Marzocco
Linea PB ABR

GRINDERS
Mahlkonig
Tanzania,
Mazzer Major

OPENING HOURS
Mon-Sat 8am-6pm
Sun 11am-4pm

BEANS AVAILABLE INSTORE

ALTERNATIVE MILK

WIFI

T: 07595 171846
f Espresso Corner ⊙ @espressocorner

MAP 92. THE HANDMADE BAKERY

Unit 6, Upper Mills Canal Side, Slaithwaite, Huddersfield, West Yorkshire, HD7 5HA

Bread bonds may not be legal tender in England but it was the promise of weekly loaves to locals that allowed this innovative cooperative to expand and add a cafe to its blooming bakery business.

Dark Woods Coffee (roasted half a mile down the road) is served in a range of espresso based drinks, along with a menu of baked beauties from breakfast through to lunch.

Try the Lincolnshire cheese-stuffed croissant, savoury danish pastries and homemade baked beans on fresh-from-the-oven sourdough for a taste of the bakery's skill.

INSIDER'S TIP GRAB A BAG OF DARK WOODS COFFEE WITH YOUR SOURDOUGH TO-GO

If you can tear your attention from the bakers working on tomorrow's carby haul in the open kitchen, swap a pew at one of the communal benches for a sunny spot in the courtyard where you can watch narrowboats bob along the canal to Slaithwaite.

Hands-on courses at Handmade Bakery HQ are as popular as the patisserie to-go, so it's worth booking ahead if you're hungry to learn the basics of artisan bread, wild yeast or Italian baking.

ESTABLISHED
2010

KEY ROASTER
Dark Woods Coffee

BREWING METHOD
Espresso

MACHINE
Sanremo

GRINDER
Sanremo

OPENING HOURS
Tue-Sun
9.30am-4.30pm

---

www.thehandmadebakery.coop   T: 01484 842175

f The Handmade Bakery   @handmadebakery   @thehandmadebakery

№93. BLOC

19a Huddersfield Road, Holmfirth, West Yorkshire, HD9 2JR

Opening Bloc was the realisation of a long-held dream for owner Meg: *'I'd play "cafe" for hours as a kid,'* she says. 'So *when this property came on the market, I knew I had to seize the opportunity.'*

Aged just 21 but bubbling with spirited enthusiasm, Meg honed her coffee skills with Paul at Dark Woods. Her preparation paid dividends and every cup poured at Bloc receives attention and skill, whether espresso based or pourover.

INSIDER'S TIP THE YUMMY EGGY BREAD IS JUST HOW YOU REMEMBERED IT AS A KID

Similar to the Scandinavian smørbrød (open sandwich), Bloc's menu centres around toast with delicious toppings. *'We have such a tiny kitchen that we needed to keep the menu simple,'* Meg says. *'Customers love the massive choice though, from our kickass avocado, chilli and eggs, to bananas, honey and cinnamon on toast.'*

With a fresh, colourful interior and vibrant seating area outside, the cafe is a year-round destination that would fit in just fine on the streets of Portland, Oregon. Take advantage of the blankets and heaters in winter to smug it up and make passersby jealous.

ESTABLISHED
2016

KEY ROASTER
Dark Woods
Coffee

BREWING METHODS
Espresso, V60

MACHINE
La Marzocco
Linea AV

GRINDER
Cimbali
Magnum
on demand

OPENING HOURS
Mon 9am-5pm
Wed-Sat
9am-5pm
Sun 10am-4pm

 Gluten FREE

 ALTERNATIVE MILK

 WIFI

 CYCLE FRIENDLY

 OUTDOOR seating

FAMILY FRIENDLY

DISABLED ACCESS

 BRING YOUR OWN Cup

www.bloctoast.co.uk T: 01484 687228
f Bloc 🐦 @bloc_holmfirth 📷 @bloc_holmfirth

94. ARTEMIS COLD BREW COFFEE

Womersley, North Yorkshire, DN6 9BB

It's the creamiest, smoothest nitro cold brew imaginable, with a long and beautiful cascade – a unique and covetable experience for any coffee connoisseur. Last year Artemis' nitro cold brew became available on draught, much to the delight of coffee drinkers and coffee shop owners across the UK.

The guys' pioneering spirit doesn't stop there however, and they're now tackling a completely different beast: the cocktail market. In July, they launched a cold brew coffee concentrate, a useful ingredient in the crafting of coffee cocktails. Like Artemis' bottled cold brew, the product is fully natural, consisting of only coffee and water.

'Coffee quality is often the last thing on a bar owner's mind, so we're working with roasters North Star to change this,' says managing director, Ben Barker. *'Coffee can be such a brilliant flavour in cocktails – whether dominant or simply a nuance – but it's often overlooked.'*

Using the world's first cold brew concentrate made to the same strength as espresso (yet with the benefits of cold brew) creating coffee cocktails is now as simple as pouring a shot.

'COFFEE CAN BE SUCH A BRILLIANT FLAVOUR IN COCKTAILS – WHETHER IT IS DOMINANT OR SIMPLY A NUANCE – BUT IT'S OFTEN OVERLOOKED'

'It cuts in half the time it takes to make an espresso martini while providing quality and consistency,' adds Ben. *'Getting creative with coffee and cocktails has never been so accessible.'*

Since launching two years ago, Artemis have become the go-to guys for cold brew, with bottles and nitro on draught sold in more than 50 UK indies. An unshakeable passion for quality, sustainability and traceability, meanwhile, has earned them the first Great Taste Award for cold brew coffee.

www.artemisbrew.co.uk   T: 01977 621691

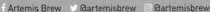

f Artemis Brew   🐦 @artemisbrew   📷 @artemisbrew

ROASTERS

> **DARK WOODS COFFEE №99**

95. ROUNTON COFFEE ROASTERS

East Rounton, Northallerton, North Yorkshire, DL6 2LG

Rounton Coffee is made up of a hard-working team of Daves. They all have coffee running through their veins, work tirelessly to get the best out of the beans and provide fantastic service to their customers.

The initial spark for the business was ignited when Dave One (owner and founder David Beattie) visited Sumatra. After spending time with the country's inspirational coffee farmers, he resolved to create a sustainable trail back to the UK market.

ESTABLISHED
2013

ROASTER
MAKE & SIZE
Toper
10kg

OPEN
BY APPOINTMENT

COFFEE
COURSES

BEANS
AVAILABLE

A NEW WEBSITE SHOWCASES THE COFFEES, A RANGE OF COFFEE MACHINES AND A POPULAR SUBSCRIPTION SERVICE

Opening a small indie coffee roastery in the picturesque North Yorkshire village of East Rounton, he continues to focus on quality seasonal and sustainable coffee. Dave Two (head roaster and green bean buyer David Burton) is usually found sourcing the finest speciality he can get his hands on and whistling in front of the roaster. Dave Three (David Atkinson aka Bruce) drives quality control as head barista, while Dave Four (David Bland) is the new head chef.

The Rounton team, which already operates Bedford St Coffee in the heart of Middlesbrough, recently launched a second outlet: The Joiners Shop in Ingleby Cross, which offers good food alongside that freshly roasted coffee.

www.rountoncoffee.co.uk   T: 07539 285197

Rounton Coffee Roasters   @rountoncoffee   @rountoncoffee

96. ROOST COFFEE & ROASTERY

M.A.P.96.

6 Talbot Yard, Yorkersgate, Malton, North Yorkshire, YO17 7FT

Among an enterprising and innovative cluster of entrepreneurs in the food production court at Talbot Yard is Roost Coffee and Roastery.

Owned by David and Ruth Elkington – aided in their endeavours by daughters and young-baristas-in-the-making Erin and Betsy – the business is part of a community of artisan producers who unite under the slogan 'Made in Malton'.

At the Diedrich roaster, David reads the beans to create exquisite espresso blends including the popular full bodied and smooth Roost Espresso and darker Tonto Espresso. Coffee shops, hotels and restaurants snap up small batches of these freshly roasted espressos, single origins and Swiss Water decaf.

ESTABLISHED
2015

ROASTER
MAKE & SIZE
Diedrich IR-12
12kg

CAFE
ONSITE

OPEN
BY APPOINTMENT

OPEN
TO THE PUBLIC

COFFEE
COURSES

BEANS
AVAILABLE
ONSITE

'WE'RE HAPPY TO BE A PART OF THE "MADE IN MALTON" FAMILY. MALTON IS NOW FIRMLY ON THE MAP AS YORKSHIRE'S FOOD CAPITAL'

And the good news is that everyone is invited to drop by for a bag or mug of their fave brew; the in-house espresso bar (open Wed-Sat, 10am-2pm) is a chance to experience coffee pulled through the Rocket Espresso Milano or enjoyed as a pourover filter.

Roost is also a distributor of commercial and domestic Rocket Espresso machines.

www.roostcoffee.co.uk   T: 01653 697635

f Roost Coffee   🐦 @roost_coffee   📷 @roost_coffee

M.A.P. No. 97. YORK COFFEE EMPORIUM

Unit 4-5 Rose Centre, Rose Avenue, York Business Park, York, North Yorkshire, YO26 6RX

Lovingly orchestrated by Laurence and Philippa Beardmore, this passionately-operated roasting outfit is fuelled by the couple's desire to help educate and satisfy a growing and loyal customer base of coffee fiends.

Taking over the business five years ago, the pair swear by morning team briefings and profile tasting sessions to ensure consistency in their range of small batch roasts.

Using a variety of roasters, including their reconditioned vintage Otto Swadlo traditional drum roaster, and sourcing beans from small speciality farms, the team have earned an award winning reputation across the North and firmly cemented their place in the UK roasting scene.

ESTABLISHED
2012

ROASTER
MAKE & SIZE
Probat 25kg
Sivetz 18kg
Otto Swadlo 5kg
Solar 2kg

OPEN
BY APPOINTMENT

COFFEE
COURSES

BEANS
AVAILABLE
ONSITE
ONLINE

THE NINTH BLEND IS NAMED AFTER JULIUS CAESAR'S NINTH ROMAN LEGION WHICH BUILT THE FIRST ROMAN FORT IN YORK

Customer care is key, and cafes are offered bespoke blends and personalised packaging.

A subscription service allows home brewers to get in on the action too, with Q grader Laurence providing monthly blogs, tips and recommendations, while consumers are also invited to take part in roastery tours.

www.yorkcoffeeemporium.co.uk T: 01904 799399

 York Coffee Emporium 🐦 @york_coffee 📷 @yorkcoffeeemporium

MAP №98. CIELO COFFEE

41 Main Street, Garforth, Leeds, West Yorkshire, LS25 1DS

Cielo is a shining example of how coffee can be the catalyst to instigate positive social change.

Set up by Nick and Linda Castle as a social enterprise cafe in 2008, Cielo has blossomed into a multifaceted organisation. It now has a roastery in Garforth and six cafes across Leeds which supply their neighbourhoods with both great coffee and a community hub.

And in addition to donating 65% of the profits to community causes (both nearby and further afield), it also creates work experience opportunities for locals who gain skills for hospitality roles through its voluntary work scheme.

ONE OF THE PROJECTS SUPPORTED BY CIELO HELPS ETHIOPIAN CHILDREN WHO HAVE CLUB FOOT

The focus on coffee quality is just as keen as the desire to do good, and the crew roast single origin, ethically sourced beans from around the world on their 5kg Probatone. Farmer information is made available to customers to educate them and involve them in the Cielo mission.

In addition to the single origins, choose between two espresso blends: Presenza (chocolate, nut) and East Gate (fruity, sweet), which is also the Cielo cafe espresso choice.

ESTABLISHED
2008

ROASTER
MAKE & SIZE
Probat
Probatone
5kg

CAFE ONSITE

OPEN BY APPOINTMENT

COFFEE COURSES

BEANS AVAILABLE
ONSITE

ONLINE

www.cielouk.com T: 01132 863534
f Cielo Coffee 🐦 @cielouk 📷 @cielocoffee

MAP 99. DARK WOODS COFFEE

Holme Mills, West Slaithwaite Road, Marsden, Huddersfield, West Yorkshire, HD7 6LS

Roasting from a renovated Victorian mill on the banks of the River Colne, Dark Woods is a company of contrasts.

The tranquil setting and heritage exterior belie the bright and modern roasting and training space, while the relaxed and inclusive approach to coffee shouldn't distract from a rotating seasonal list which features some of the most exclusive micro lots available in the UK.

The team centres on directors and founders Paul, Ian and Damian, who between them have major experience in international competition judging, green coffee buying and high-end coffee consultancy.

'A ROTATING SEASONAL LIST FEATURES SOME OF THE MOST EXCLUSIVE MICRO LOTS AVAILABLE IN THE UK'

And from Michelin starred restaurants and London department stores to local bakeries and speciality coffee shops, Dark Woods' beautifully packaged beans awaken the palates of curious coffee lovers across the country.

The lovingly restored 1950s Probat UG 22 recently gave birth to a bouncing baby 5kg Probatone. A new addition which will enable roaster Damian to further develop the flavour potential of existing blends and offer an ever-more varied and diverse range of exclusive single estate coffees.

ESTABLISHED
2013

ROASTERS
MAKE & SIZE
Vintage Probat
UG 22,
Probatone 5

CAFE
ONSITE

OPEN
BY APPOINTMENT

COFFEE
COURSES

COURSES

BEANS
AVAILABLE
ONSITE

ONLINE

www.darkwoodscoffee.co.uk   T: 01484 843141

f Dark Woods Coffee   @darkwoodscoffee   @darkwoodscoffee

FAIRTRADE BEGINS AT HOME

STEPHENSONS DAIRY BECOME FIRST TO LAUNCH
FREE RANGE MILK IN THE UK

1 Freightway, Morecambe LA3 3PB

01524 388688   hello@stephensonsdairy.co.uk

WWW.STEPHENSONSDAIRY.CO.UK

MAP 100. GRUMPY MULE

Bewley's, Bent Ley Road, Meltham, Holmfirth, West Yorkshire, HD9 4EP

It was once mules, not lorries, which hauled coffee cherries down mountains. So it's no surprise that the heroic animal has become the icon of a specialist roastery nestled in the rolling hills of the Holme valley.

The team certainly work like mules: they've crafted 28 Great Taste Award winners in the last three years. Two trusty Probat drum roasters and a Loring Smart roaster keep the batch size and roast profile flexible to tease out the subtle flavours in each coffee.

ESTABLISHED
2006

ROASTER
MAKE & SIZE
Probat G120
Probat G60
Loring Kestrel
35kg

COFFEE COURSES

BEANS AVAILABLE

ONLINE

'WE'RE PROUD TO OFFER GREAT QUALITY BOTH IN SMALL BATCHES AND AT SCALE. GRUMPY MULE AIMS TO PUT A SMILE ON YOUR FACE WITH ITS TONGUE-IN-CHEEK, NO-NONSENSE BRAND'

The team hold to ethical standards that benefit everyone, whether that's through Fairtrade, direct trade or working with organic farmers and growers.

'Dedicated to speciality coffee, the mule is excited to tell it like it is,' smiles Gemma Astbury.

And where does the 'grumpy' bit come in? We reckon we'd be pretty disgruntled if we had to carry coffee cherries down a mountain.

www.grumpymule.co.uk   T: 01484 852601
f Grumpy Mule   🐦 @grumpymule   📷 @grumpy_mule

SOUTH AND EAST YORKSHIRE & LINCOLNSHIRE

> TAMPER – WESTFIELD TERRACE №107

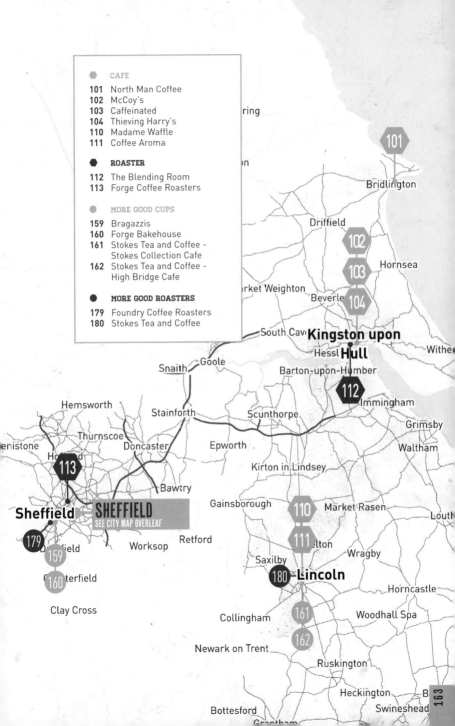

CAFE

101 North Man Coffee
102 McCoy's
103 Caffeinated
104 Thieving Harry's
110 Madame Waffle
111 Coffee Aroma

ROASTER

112 The Blending Room
113 Forge Coffee Roasters

MORE GOOD CUPS

159 Bragazzis
160 Forge Bakehouse
161 Stokes Tea and Coffee -
    Stokes Collection Cafe
162 Stokes Tea and Coffee -
    High Bridge Cafe

MORE GOOD ROASTERS

179 Foundry Coffee Roasters
180 Stokes Tea and Coffee

Bridlington

Driffield

Hornsea

Market Weighton

Beverle

South Cave

Kingston upon

Hessl Hull

Wither

Barton-upon-Humber

Snaith Goole

Immingham

Hemsworth

Stainforth

Scunthorpe

Grimsby

Thurnscoe

Doncaster

Epworth

Waltham

enistone

Ho d

Kirton in Lindsey

Bawtry

Gainsborough

Market Rasen

Louth

Sheffield

SHEFFIELD
SEE CITY MAP OVERLEAF

Worksop Retford

Saxilby

Wragby

field

Horncastle

terfield

Lincoln

Clay Cross

Collingham

Woodhall Spa

Newark on Trent

Ruskington

Heckington

Bottesford

Swineshead

SHEFFIELD

CAFE

105 The Depot Eatery
106 Upshot
107 Tamper - Westfield Terrace
108 Marmadukes Cafe Deli
109 Tamper - Sellers Wheel

MORE GOOD CUPS

158 Steam Yard

MORE GOOD ROASTERS

178 Smith Street Coffee Roasters

MAP 101. NORTH MAN COFFEE

7 Manor Street, Bridlington, East Yorkshire, YO15 2SA

I f the waft of freshly brewed coffee doesn't lure you into this welcoming spot, the scent of just-baked loaves and cakes surely will.

Not content with simply introducing the good folk of Bridlington to great brews by the likes of Square Mile and Workshop, North Man Coffee is also on a mission to wow visitors with fresh-from-the-oven thrills.

'Although we've always made all our bread on site, we've recently started selling it too, with three or four varieties of organic loaves available,' says Oakley Wheelwright.

INSIDER'S TIP GET IN EARLY TO BAG FRESHLY BAKED BREAD – IT DOESN'T HANG AROUND FOR LONG

The team are obsessive when it comes to consistent, high quality coffee, and this even extends to the latte art.

'Nothing puts a smile on a customer's face like a nice clean tulip,' says Oakley.

The tradition of hospitality runs in the family at this contemporary restaurant, which is also known for its inventive veggie and vegan offerings.

'It's fantastic to see customers who've supported generations of Wheelwrights, helping us thrive,' he says. *'My mother Katy, who is a baker extraordinaire, still gets up at 5am to bake our cakes each day.'*

ESTABLISHED
2016

KEY ROASTER
Square Mile
Coffee Roasters

BREWING METHODS
Espresso,
Kalita Wave,
AeroPress

MACHINE
La Marzocco
FB80

GRINDER
Mythos One

OPENING HOURS
Mon-Sat
8am-5pm
Sun
10am-3pm

T: 07932 569129
f North Man Coffee 🐦 @northmancoffee 📷 @northmancoffee

102. McCOY'S

Colonial Chambers, 32 Princes Dock Street, Hull, East Yorkshire, HU1 2JX

A winter snug next to a roaring log fire, a suntrap to soak up the rays and a quayside view to catch the cool breeze while sipping a latte – it's little wonder this grand double-fronted Victorian coffee emporium on four floors, has been a favourite with locals and visitors for over a decade.

And short of growing the beans themselves, you'd be hard pushed to find fresher coffee. Ten different origin beans are roasted in-house in small batches before grinding and brewing, making the whole place smell sensational. Tell the cheery crew your flavour preference and they'll create the perfect cup for you, whether it's espresso based, a pourover or Swiss water decaf.

INSIDER'S TIP SIGN UP FOR THE NEWSLETTER TO GET A FREE COFFEE SAMPLE, PLUS NEWS ON DISCOUNTS

The discerning coffee connoisseur is kept happy alongside thirsty customers perusing the long list of teas, hot chocolate and boozy tipples. Come lunchtime, whatever your appetite, you'll be spoilt for choice with sharing platters, pies, salads and sandwiches to suit all. And don't forget to buy a bag of the magic beans to take home afterwards.

ESTABLISHED
2002

KEY ROASTER
McCoy's

BREWING METHODS
Espresso, drip,
Chemex,
cold brew

MACHINE
Ladri

GRINDER
Mazzer on
demand

OPENING HOURS
Mon-Sat
8am-6pm
Sun
9.30am-4pm

---

www.mccoyshull.co.uk   T: 01482 327757

f McCoy's Coffee   🐦 @mccoyscoffee   📷 @mccoyscoffee

MAP 103. CAFFEINATED

Trinity Indoor Market, Market Lane, Hull, East Yorkshire, HU1 2JH

Trinity Market first opened its doors to Edwardian punters 115 years ago, and hadn't significantly changed until a recent refurbishment transformed the space to attract an array of artisans to this corner of Old Town Hull.

Quietly crafting top quality coffee and beautiful bakes from the bustling hubbub are Joe Martin and Mikeala Hall, the coffee obsessed duo behind the market's first speciality cafe.

INSIDER'S TIP LOOK OUT FOR GUESTS SUCH AS SQUARE MILE, EXTRACT AND NUDE ON FILTER

Local micro roaster The Blending Room provides the goods for Caffeinated's espresso blend while the guest beans take punters on a whirlwind tour of European roasteries.

'We buy our guest beans to be challenging,' explains Joe. *'And endeavour to widen our customers' coffee experience by demonstrating the exciting, complex and memorable opportunities in each cup.'*

Pair your pick with a treat from Mikeala's creative kitchen such as Oreo and raspberry tart, and cream cheese frosted pumpkin bundt cake.

ESTABLISHED
2015

KEY ROASTER
The Blending Room

BREWING METHODS
Espresso, V60, AeroPress, Clever Dripper, drip brewer

MACHINES
Nuova Simonelli Aurelia II

GRINDERS
Eureka Mythos, Mahlkonig Tanzania, Macap MXD

OPENING HOURS
Mon-Fri 7.30am-4pm
Sat 8.30am-4.30pm
Sun 10.30am-3.30pm

BEANS AVAILABLE INSTORE

MILK

CYCLE FRIENDLY

FAMILY FRIENDLY

DISABLED ACCESS

T: 07927 832031

f Caffeinated 🐦 @caffeinatedhull @ @caffeinated_hull

MAP 104. THIEVING HARRY'S

73 Humber Street, Hull, East Yorkshire, HU1 1TU

Doing more successful pop-ups than a jack-in-the-box, family-run coffee shop and restaurant Thieving Harry's has been brewing up a storm in Hull since 2011. And due to popular demand, the team now have a permanent home in Hull's former fruit market.

Surrounded by cultural cool and views of boats bobbing on the marina, this is a crafty caffeine pit-stop with a bit of people watching thrown in.

INSIDER'S TIP: THE PLACE PUMPS ON DJ NIGHTS. FOLLOW ON FACEBOOK FOR EVENT DEETS

You can also recharge your evening here with an espresso martini. With vibrant nightlife on its doorstep, Thieving Harry's has extended its opening hours to offer dinner and a unique craft, draft and spirits selection.

Coffee lovers should visit for the single origin guest beans from the likes of Workshop and Caravan, and stay for the sensational grilled cheese sandwiches (note: order with tomato chilli jam, avocado and extra bacon). Then let Thieving Harry's steal your heart with one of its fiendishly naughty brownies.

ESTABLISHED
2011

KEY ROASTER
The Blending Room

BREWING METHODS
Espresso, V60, AeroPress, batch filter

MACHINE
Sanremo Zoe

GRINDERS
Nuova Simonelli Mythos One, Mahlkonig EK 43

OPENING HOURS
Mon 10am-late
Tue-Wed 10am-4pm
Thu-Fri 10am-late
Sat-Sun 9am-late

www.thievingharrys.co.uk T: 01482 214141
f Thieving Harry's 🐦 @thievingharrys 📷 @thieving_harrys

105. THE DEPOT EATERY

92 Burton Road, Sheffield, South Yorkshire, S3 8DA

The latest incarnation of the Tamper experience, The Depot Eatery introduces Kiwi coffee cool and artisan bakery thrills to the hiply industrial Kelham Island.

Pared back and funky with hanging plants and a gritty city mural, the cafe – which adjoins The Depot Bakery – is also your go-to for takeaway loaves of chewy sourdough, homemade focaccia and hand crafted patisserie (note: the passion fruit curd stuffed doughnuts are to die for).

A little walk from the centre of the city, you'll want to linger for delicious eggs on sourdough with your batch brew or espresso.

INSIDER'S TIP CHECK OUT THE MONTHLY CHANGING MENU OF BAKERY PRODUCE AND SAVOURY DISHES

Or visit on the last Friday and Saturday of every month when the vibrant Peddler street food event springs up around the cafe, with music, cocktails, wood fired pizza and dim sum all complementing the caffeinated, carb-tastic Depot staples.

ESTABLISHED
2014

KEY ROASTER
Ozone Coffee Roasters

BREWING METHODS
Espresso, batch brew

MACHINE
La Marzocco Linea

GRINDER
Mazzer Kony

OPENING HOURS
Mon-Sun
9am-4pm

Gluten FREE

BEANS AVAILABLE INSTORE

ALTERNATIVE MILK

WIFI

CYCLE FRIENDLY

FAMILY FRIENDLY

DISABLED ACCESS

BRING YOUR OWN Cup

---

www.thedepotbakery.co.uk   T: 01142 757779

f The Depot Bakery   🐦 @thedepotbakery   📷 @thedepotbakery

MAP № 106. UPSHOT

353-355 Glossop Road, Sheffield, South Yorkshire, S10 2HP

Since opening two years ago, Sam Binstead's Upshot, next to the University of Sheffield, has demonstrated a serious commitment to speciality coffee.

Sourcing from an eclectic mix of international roasters, including Round Hill, Drop, Tim Wendelboe, Bonanza and Coffee Collective, has earned it the reputation of a speciality go-to.

It's also enabled the team to launch a second cafe and bakery space in a characterful Victorian unit at Kelham Island, which will open this year.

INSIDER'S TIP BOOK ONLINE FOR TRAINING AND COFFEE COURSES

The team serve a variety of single origins across several brewing methods, loose-leaf craft teas by Lalani & Co and premium matcha in a range of bespoke stoneware by ceramicist Jono Smart.

Pair your morning brew with a homemade cinnamon bun (they're mad on 'em), or order from the Scandi-inspired all-day menu for brunch and lunch.

ESTABLISHED
2014

KEY ROASTERS
Round Hill Roastery, Drop Coffee, Bonanza Coffee, Assembly, Tim Wendelboe, The Coffee Collective

BREWING METHODS
Espresso, Kalita, Chemex, Aero-Press, batch brew

MACHINE
Kees van der Westen

GRINDERS
Mahlkonig Peak, Mahlkonig EK 43

OPENING HOURS
Mon-Fri
8am-4.30pm
Sat 9.30am-3pm

Gluten FREE

BEANS AVAILABLE INSTORE

ALTERNATIVE MILK

WIFI

COFFEE COURSES

www.upshotespresso.co.uk T: 01142 780333

f Upshot Espresso 🐦 @upshotespresso 📷 @upshotespresso

MAP Nº 107. TAMPER – WESTFIELD TERRACE

9 Westfield Terrace, Sheffield, South Yorkshire, S1 4GH

This is where the Tamper revolution kicked off, when Kiwi couple Jon and Natalie Perry introduced the delights of New Zealand cafe culture to Sheffield. And as anyone who has experienced the scene knows, great coffee is a given. And brunch? It's practically a constitutional right.

Coffee is at the heart of this operation with single origin beans from Ozone transmogrified into silky flat whites and exceptional espresso, while filter fans are well served with V60, AeroPress and syphon.

Having simultaneously built their artisan Depot Bakery business, Jon and Natalie have the edibles covered too, with seriously good sourdough and pastries available all week.

INSIDER'S TIP: TAKE PART IN THE MONTHLY, THEMED TASTING SESSIONS

'We were one of the original coffee shops in Sheffield and consistently strive to be at the top of our game through our coffee, techniques and enthusiasm for coffee,' says Jon. We'll raise a cup (and a hunk of homemade banana bread) to that.

ESTABLISHED
2011

KEY ROASTER
Ozone Coffee Roasters

BREWING METHODS
Espresso, V60, AeroPress, syphon

MACHINE
La Marzocco Strada

GRINDERS
Mythos, Mahlkonig EK 43

OPENING HOURS
Mon-Fri
8am-4.30pm
Sat 9am-4pm
Sun 10am-4pm

 Gluten FREE

 BEANS AVAILABLE INSTORE

 ALTERNATIVE MILK

 WIFI

 CYCLE FRIENDLY

 BRING YOUR OWN Cup

---

www.tampercoffee.co.uk T: 01143 271080

f Tamper Coffee 🐦 @tampercoffee 📷 @tampercoffeesw

№108. MARMADUKES CAFE DELI

22 Norfolk Row, Sheffield, South Yorkshire, S1 2PA

This beautiful little cafe near the Crucible is a must-visit for gorging, slurping or just hanging out. Grab a sunny seat out front, nab a nook in the bustling downstairs area with its accompanying hiss of the steam wand, or chill out in the tranquil first floor rooms.

Whichever you choose, you're set for cracking coffee and a bountiful brunch. Plump for scotch pancakes with vanilla berry compote, oat streusel and ice cream, or classic bacon and maple syrup – and there's plenty for the savoury-toothed too.

INSIDER'S TIP TABLE SERVICE HAS BEEN INTRODUCED SO YOU CAN JUST SIT AND SIP

Especially popular from the in-house haul is the baked cheesecake (it's practically got its own fan club), while new this year is a cocktail list which puts the recently acquired alcohol licence to good use.

Despite all this, *'Coffee is now front and centre,'* says owner Clare. Head barista Will has introduced a new house espresso from The Barn, with Round Hill, Origin and April for filter fans.

ESTABLISHED
2012

KEY ROASTER
The Barn

BREWING METHODS
Espresso, Kalita Wave, AeroPress, batch brew

MACHINE
La Marzocco Linea PB

GRINDERS
Mazzer Robur, Mahlkonig EK 43

OPENING HOURS
Mon-Sat 9am-5pm
Sun 10am-4pm

www.marmadukes.co T: 01142 767462
f Marmadukes Cafe Deli @marmadukescafe @marmadukescafe

MAP№109. TAMPER – SELLERS WHEEL
149 Arundel Street, Sheffield, South Yorkshire, S1 2NU

When Kiwi Jon Perry brought the Tamper coffee experience to Sheffield a few years ago, it was the start of something significant.

And while Westfield Terrace focused primarily on exceptional coffee, it was the launch of Sellers Wheel which took things to another level.

New Zealand cafe culture and a taste of paradise have been introduced to the Grade II-listed former silversmiths through luscious murals and trailing fronds of greenery.

INSIDER'S TIP YOU CAN ALSO HIRE THE TAMPER CREW FOR YOUR OWN EVENT

And while a cracking collection of brunch and lunch dishes and top-notch coffee delight by day, on Friday evenings it transforms into a hip hangout for craft beer and cocktails, with an innovative supper menu and late night espresso. And if you fancy your own party you can hire the joint any other night of the week.

Brunch dishes such as the Rejuvenator – homemade lime and basil hummus, parsley pesto, veggies, halloumi, pearl barley and poached egg on sourdough – have earned it the title of *Eat Sheffield*'s Best Cafe three years in a row and coveted inclusion in *The Guardian*'s Top 50 Breakfast Spots 2017.

ESTABLISHED
2013

KEY ROASTER
Ozone Coffee Roasters

BREWING METHODS
Espresso, V60, AeroPress, batch brew

MACHINE
La Marzocco Linea PB

GRINDERS
Mythos, Mahlkonig EK 43

OPENING HOURS
Mon-Thu 8am-5pm
Fri 8am-10pm
Sat 9am-6pm
Sun 9am-4pm

www.tampercoffee.co.uk T: 01142 757970
f Tamper Coffee @tampercoffee @tampercoffeesw

MAP № 110. MADAME WAFFLE

285 High Street, Lincoln, Lincolnshire, LN2 1AL

Whether you're a sucker for tradition and plump for maple syrup dusted with icing sugar, or go experimental with a mustard, roast ham, cheese sauce and egg mash-up, there's a stunning choice of Belgian-style beauties to try at Madame Waffle.

The crispy-on-the-outside-fluffy-on-the-inside sweet or savoury treats are served as breakfast, brunch, lunch and as post-meridian snacks alongside serious coffee from Square Mile.

Owner Bruce Whetton became hooked on the aroma of coffee as a child, when his father ground freshly-roasted beans. In 1997 he opened Aroma in Skegness and is now a SCA trainer of budding baristas. Wife Sharon, meanwhile, keeps the coffee lovers fed with fresh-from-the-griddle thrills.

INSIDER'S TIP
TRY THE NATURAL ETHIOPIAN BREWED ON V60. IT'S DAMN GOOD

There are three floors to explore, including an intriguing vaulted basement, a split-level ground floor and the first floor restaurant, along with a wealth of live music, cuppings, gin tastings and guest roasts from the likes of The Barn, Strangers and Makushi.

ESTABLISHED
2015

KEY ROASTER
Square Mile
Coffee Roasters

BREWING METHODS
Espresso, V60,
Chemex,
AeroPress

MACHINE
La Marzocco
Linea PB

GRINDERS
Mythos One x 2,
Mahlkonig EK 43

OPENING HOURS
Mon-Thu
8am-5pm
Fri-Sat
8am-6pm
Sun
10am-5pm

 Gluten FREE

 BEANS AVAILABLE INSTORE

 ALTERNATIVE MILK

 WIFI

 OUTDOOR SEATING

 FAMILY FRIENDLY

 BRING YOUR OWN CUP

 COFFEE COURSES

---

www.madamewaffle.co.uk   T: 01522 512286

f Madame Waffle   ✏ @madamewaffleuk   ◎ @madamewaffle

111. COFFEE AROMA

24 Guildhall Street, Lincoln, Lincolnshire, LN1 1TR

offee Aroma was cited in *The Guardian* as one of the best ten coffee shops in the UK – and it's not difficult to see why.

The array of espresso based coffee drinks at this Lincoln cafe is quite dazzling, from the simple double espresso (served with sparkling water) to the boozy special (dark mocha with Cointreau) and summery black tonic (double espresso served over Fever Tree tonic and ice).

Beans which have been lightly toasted at Stafford's Has Bean have their goodness lovingly extracted with precision by the Black Eagle Gravitech and the friendly, award winning baristas. There are plenty of options on filter, too.

INSIDER'S TIP: LOOK OUT FOR LIVE MUSIC, STREET PARTIES AND COMEDY ON THE WEEKENDS

These are not the only potable pleasures at this quirkily decorated cafe which is spread over three floors. Hot chocolate, loose-leaf teas, cascara, chai, ales, wines and coffee cocktails are best imbibed with the likes of a meat and cheese platter, blueberry tulip muffin or a fresh-from-the-oven pain au chocolate in one of the many cosy nooks.

ESTABLISHED
2005

KEY ROASTER
Has Bean Coffee

BREWING METHODS
Espresso, Chemex, V60, AeroPress, cold brew

MACHINE
Victoria Arduino VA388 Black Eagle Gravitech

GRINDERS
Mahlkonig K30 Vario, Mahlkonig Tanzania

OPENING HOURS
Mon-Thu
8am-7pm
Fri-Sat 8am-11pm
Sun 10am-5pm

 Gluten FREE

 BEANS AVAILABLE INSTORE

 ALTERNATIVE MILK

 WIFI

 OUTDOOR Seating

 FAMILY FRIENDLY

---

www.coffeearoma.co.uk   T: 01522 569892

 Coffee Aroma   @coffee_aroma   @aromacoffeehouse

ROASTERS

MAP № 112. THE BLENDING ROOM

Unit 22 Factory Estate, Boulevard, Hull, East Yorkshire, HU3 4AY

After 16 years' experience in the coffee industry, James and Katie are as obsessed as ever with the pursuit of the perfect cup of coffee.

'Our aim is to challenge perceptions of what coffee can taste like,' says James, and the pair focus on finding the ideal ratio of sweetness to acidity in order to best accentuate each batch of beans' unique flavour profile.

They take the fine art of caffeine consumption seriously and lavish great attention on the entire roasting process in which beans from a wide variety of origins are cooked up on a Diedrich IR3 and Probat P12 II.

ESTABLISHED
2009

ROASTER
MAKE & SIZE
Probat P12
12kg
Diedrich IR-3
3kg

OPEN
BY APPOINTMENT

BEANS
AVAILABLE

ONSITE

ONLINE

'OUR AIM IS TO CHALLENGE PERCEPTIONS OF WHAT COFFEE CAN TASTE LIKE'

'We work closely with our importers to expose ourselves to a broad spectrum of coffee,' says James.

As each delivery of green coffee changes with the season, terroir and processing, every roasted batch is tasted many times before being given a stamp of approval.

When they aren't roasting, grinding, blending, brewing and pouring, you'll find James and Katie on their market stall in Beverley on Saturday mornings. Stop by to say hello – either at the market, or at the roastery itself.

www.theblendingroom.co.uk T: 01482 212409

f The Blending Room 🐦 @theblendingroom 📷 @theblendingroom

113. FORGE COFFEE ROASTERS

Don Road, Sheffield, South Yorkshire, S9 2TF

Inspired by the master craftsmen who once toiled in the city of steel, Forge has crafted a roastery of the highest quality, artistry and creativity.

'We're bonkers about beans, brews and bikes,' say Michael (who runs the business) and Jack (who roasts the coffee), *'and we want to put Sheffield on the UK roasting map.'*

With the city's industrial heritage as their motivation, the team utilise the latest technology from Ikawa for sample roasting and a treasured Giesen W30A. *'We thrive on developing outstanding coffee and passing our knowledge and passion on to our customers,'* says Michael.

'INSPIRED BY THE MASTER CRAFTSMEN WHO ONCE TOILED IN THE CITY OF STEEL'

In addition to roasting, researching, training and fine tuning brewing equipment, the 20-strong Forge crew also take their handcrafted coffee on the road to selected events. Look out for the 1935 Bedford truck (Bar 124) and a gorgeous 1933 Austin 7 van which are fully equipped to provide high quality coffee brewing action.

ESTABLISHED
2015

ROASTER
MAKE & SIZE
Giesen
30kg

OPEN
BY APPOINTMENT

COFFEE
COURSES

BEANS
AVAILABLE

ONSITE

ONLINE

---

www.forgecoffeeroasters.co.uk   T: 01142 441361

f Forge Coffee Roasters   🐦 @forgeroasters   📷 @forgeroasters

MORE GOOD CUPS

So many exceptional places to drink coffee …

MAP № 122
OPPOSITE CAFE – CHAPEL ALLERTON
4 Stainbeck Lane, Leeds,
West Yorkshire, LS7 3QY

MAP № 123
PUMP N GRIND
52 Brudenell Road, Leeds,
West Yorkshire, LS6 1BD

www.pumpngrind.co.uk

MAP № 124
OPPOSITE CAFE – BLENHEIM TERRACE
26 Blenheim Terrace, Leeds,
West Yorkshire, LS2 9HD

MAP № 125
SOCIABLE FOLK
10 Wellington Place, Leeds,
West Yorkshire, LS1 4AP

www.sociablefolk.co.uk

MAP № 126
CIELO COFFEE – YORK PLACE
18 York Place, Leeds,
West Yorkshire, LS1 2EX

www.cielouk.com

MAP № 127
CIELO COFFEE – DUNCAN STREET
Unit 2, 7 Duncan Street, Leeds,
West Yorkshire, LS1 6DQ

www.cielouk.com

MAP № 128
MRS ATHA'S
Central Road, Leeds, West Yorkshire, LS1 6DE

www.mrsathasleeds.com

MAP № 129
KAPOW COFFEE – THE CALLS
44 The Calls, Leeds,
West Yorkshire, LS2 7EW

MAP № 130
CAFÉ 164
Munro House, Duke Street, Leeds,
West Yorkshire, LS9 8AG

www.cafe164.com

MAP № 131
CIELO COFFEE – CROSSGATES
Unit 13, Crossgates Shopping Centre,
Leeds, West Yorkshire, LS15 8ET

www.cielouk.com

MAP № 132
CIELO COFFEE – GARFORTH
41 Main Street, Garforth, Leeds,
West Yorkshire, LS25 1DS

www.cielouk.com

133
CIELO COFFEE – EXPRESS
1-5 Main Street, Leeds,
West Yorkshire, LS25 1DU

www.cielouk.com

134
EXCHANGE COFFEE COMPANY – SKIPTON
10 Gargrave Road, Skipton,
North Yorkshire, BD23 1PJ

www.exchangecoffee.co.uk

135
TOAST HOUSE
22 Leeds Road, Ilkley,
West Yorkshire, LS29 8DS

www.toasthouse.co.uk

136
EMILY'S BY DE LUCA BOUTIQUE
72-74 Market Street, Thornton, Bradford,
West Yorkshire, BD13 3HF

www.delucaboutique.co.uk

137
EXCHANGE COFFEE COMPANY – TODMORDEN
Market Hall, Burnley Road, Todmorden,
West Yorkshire, OL14 5AJ

www.exchangecoffee.co.uk

138
EXCHANGE COFFEE COMPANY – BLACKBURN MARKET
Stall F9/1 Blackburn Market,
Ainsworth Street, Blackburn,
Lancashire, BB1 5AF

www.exchangecoffee.co.uk

139
PANNA KITCHEN & CANTEEN
Silk House Court, Tithebarn Street,
Liverpool, Merseyside, L2 2LZ

www.pannaliverpool.com

140
FILTER + FOX
27 Duke Street, Liverpool,
Merseyside, L1 5AP

www.filterandfox.co.uk

141
COFFEE & FANDISHA
5 Brick Street, Liverpool,
Merseyside, L1 0BL

www.coffeefandisha.com

142
BLOOMING SKULL COFFEE
138 Bebington Road, New Ferry,
Wirral, Merseyside, CH62 5BJ

www.bloomingskullcoffee.co.uk

143
THE BARISTA'S
9 Watergate Street, Chester,
Cheshire, CH1 2LB

www.thebaristas.co.uk

144
JAUNTY GOAT COFFEE
57 Bridge Street, Chester,
Cheshire, CH1 1NG

www.jauntygoatcoffee.co.uk

145
PROVIDERO –
LLANDUDNO JUNCTION
148 Conway Road, Llandudno Junction,
Conwy, LL31 9DU

146
POPUP BIKES
Arch 5, Corporation Street,
Manchester, M4 4DG

www.popupbikes.co.uk

147
ANOTHER HEART TO FEED
77-79 Chapel Street,
Manchester, M3 5BZ

www.anotherhearttofeed.com

148
GRINDSMITH – THE POD
Greengate Square, Victoria Bridge Street,
Manchester, M3 5AS

www.grindsmith.com

149
TEACUP KITCHEN
53-55 Thomas Street,
Manchester, M4 1NA

www.teacupandcakes.com

150
NORTH TEA POWER
36 Tib Street, Manchester, M4 1LA

www.northteapower.co.uk

151
IDLE HANDS
www.idlehandscoffee.com

152
EZRA & GIL
20 Hilton Street, Manchester, M1 1FR

www.ezraandgil.com

153
ANCOATS COFFEE CO.
Unit 9, Royal Mills, 17 Redhill Street,
Ancoats, Manchester, M4 5BA

www.ancoats-coffee.co.uk

154
THE ANCHOR COFFEE HOUSE
508 Moss Lane East,
Manchester, M14 4PA

www.anchorcoffee.co.uk

MAP Nº 155
TEA HIVE
53 Manchester Road, Chorlton,
Manchester, M21 9PW

www.teahive.co.uk

MAP Nº 156
TANDEM COFFEE HOUSE
47 Lower Hillgate, Stockport,
Greater Manchester, SK1 1JQ

www.tandemcoffeehouse.co.uk

MAP Nº 157
MARKET HOUSE COFFEE
Altrincham Market House,
26 Market Street, Altrincham,
Greater Manchester, WA14 1SA

www.altrinchammarket.co.uk

MAP Nº 158
STEAM YARD
Unit 1-2 Aberdeen Court,
97 Division Street, Sheffield,
South Yorkshire, S1 4GE

www.steamyard.co.uk

MAP Nº 159
BRAGAZZIS
224-226 Abbeydale Road, Sheffield,
South Yorkshire, S7 1FL

www.bragazzis.co.uk

MAP Nº 160
FORGE BAKEHOUSE
302 Abbeydale Road, Sheffield,
South Yorkshire, S7 1FL

www.forgebakehouse.co.uk

MAP Nº 161
STOKES TEA AND COFFEE – STOKES COLLECTION CAFE
Danes Terrace, Lincoln,
Lincolnshire, LN2 1LP

www.stokes-coffee.co.uk

MAP Nº 162
STOKES TEA AND COFFEE – HIGH BRIDGE CAFE
207 High Street, Lincoln,
Lincolnshire, LN5 7AU

www.stokes-coffee.co.uk

DON'T BE BLAND

Working with the best food, drink, hospitality and tourism businesses.
Call us to add a pinch of salt to your
branding, design, copywriting and magazines

salt media

MORE GOOD ROASTERS

Additional hot hauls for your hopper

MAP № 163
LUCKIE BEANS
3 Love Lane, Berwick upon Tweed,
Northumberland, TD15 1AR

www.luckiebeans.co.uk

MAP № 164
NORTHERN EDGE COFFEE
Unit 5, Meantime Workshops,
North Greenwich Road,
Spittal, Berwick upon Tweed,
Northumberland, TD15 1RG

www.northernedgecoffee.co.uk

MAP № 165
PINK LANE ROASTERY
19 Back Goldspink Lane,
Newcastle upon Tyne, NE2 1NU

www.pinklanecoffee.co.uk

MAP № 166
PUMPHREYS COFFEE
Bridge Street, Blaydon,
Newcastle upon Tyne, NE21 4JH

www.pumphreys-coffee.co.uk

MAP № 167
BEAN MILES
27 Greenacres, Wetheral, Carlisle,
Cumbria, CA4 8LD

www.beanmiles.co.uk

MAP № 168
JOLLY BEAN ROASTERY
15 Victoria Road, Saltaire,
West Yorkshire, BD18 3LQ

www.jollybeanroastery.co.uk

MAP № 169
CASA ESPRESSO
Unit 5, Briar Rhydding House,
Otley Road, Shipley, West Yorkshire,
BD17 7JW

www.casaespresso.co.uk

MAP № 170
PUMP N GRIND
52a Brudenell Road, Leeds,
West Yorkshire, LS6 1BD

www.pumpngrind.co.uk

MAP 171
MAUDE COFFEE ROASTERS
82-83 Railway Street, Leeds,
West Yorkshire, LS9 8HB

www.maudecoffee.co.uk

MAP 172
NORTH STAR COFFEE ROASTERS
Unit 33, The Boulevard, Leeds Dock,
Leeds, West Yorkshire, LS10 1PZ

www.northstarroast.com

MAP 173
HEART AND GRAFT COFFEE ROASTERY
Artwork Atelier, 95 Greengate, Salford,
Greater Manchester, M3 7NG

www.heartandgraft.co.uk

MAP 174
ANCOATS COFFEE CO.
Unit 9, Royal Mills, 17 Redhill Street,
Ancoats, Manchester, M4 5BA

www.ancoats-coffee.co.uk

MAP 175
MANCOCO
Arch 84, Hewitt Street, Manchester, M15 4GB

www.mancoco.co.uk

MAP 176
TANK COFFEE
Unit 1, Acorn Business Centre, Leigh,
Greater Manchester, WN7 3DD

www.tankcoffee.com

MAP 177
92 DEGREES COFFEE
24 Hardman Street, Liverpool,
Merseyside, L1 9AX

www.92degreescoffee.com

MAP 178
SMITH STREET COFFEE ROASTERS
156 Arundel Street, Sheffield,
South Yorkshire, S1 4RE

www.smithstreetcoffeeroasters.co.uk

MAP 179
FOUNDRY COFFEE ROASTERS
The Old Coach House, 9a Nether Edge Road,
Sheffield, South Yorkshire, S7 1RU

www.foundrycoffeeroasters.com

MAP 180
STOKES TEA AND COFFEE
Suite 1, The Lawn, Union Road, Lincoln,
Lincolnshire, LN1 3BU

www.stokes-coffee.co.uk

MEET OUR COMMITTEE

Our *Independent Coffee Guide* committee is made up of a small band of leading coffee experts from across the region who have worked with Salt Media and the North's coffee community to oversee the creation of this book

DAVE OLEJNIK

Having always sought out great coffee shops, it was during Dave's time living in Seattle (where he worked as a touring guitar tech), that he was inspired to divert his energies into coffee. Returning to the UK, he worked for Coffee Community and travelled the world as a trainer and consultant, before launching Laynes Espresso in Leeds in 2011.

Knocking through into a neighbouring building at the start of 2017, he's increased the popular cafe's capacity from 15 to 55 covers.

HANNAH DAVIES

Hannah's 11-year career in the coffee industry has seen her develop from a barista in Liverpool to training manager and authorised SCA (Speciality Coffee Association) trainer for a national coffee company. Her current role as SCA event manager allows her to fulfil her commitment to the coffee community in the UK and across Europe. Since 2014, Hannah has worked with the Manchester coffee scene to create Manchester Coffee Festival, dedicated to showcasing the speciality coffee industry in the North.

PAUL MEIKLE-JANNEY

Paul began working in coffee in 1999 when he started his barista training and coffee consultancy, Coffee Community. Passionate about education, he helped write the City and Guilds and SCA barista qualifications, and currently sits on the SCA Education Committee (he's chair of its Creators Group). Paul co-founded Dark Woods Coffee in 2014 and has been involved in the World and UK Barista Championships from the start, as well as being head judge at the World Latte Art Championship and World Coffee in Good Spirits Championship. Paul's DJ career has recently been brought out of retirement; a set of decks at the Victorian mill roastery has resulted in the team being *subjected to a lot of jazz and deep house while roasting*.

IAN STEEL

Ian has enjoyed two careers: as a TV producer and a coffee roaster, *'Both related,'* he says, *'as they involve seeing ideas through from conception to completion'*. A vital part of his current role is telling the stories of farmers to the coffee drinking public.

By concentrating on quality and investing – both locally and in initiatives at origin – Atkinsons roastery aims to add value for the consumers and producers at each end of the chain. Sustainability is also high on Ian's agenda: *'We've added an eco-roastery to the heart of Lancaster under one living roof.'*

After the success of his two speciality coffee shops in Lancaster, an exciting new venture in Manchester's Northern Quarter will join the Atkinsons clan in late 2017.

COFFEE NOTES

Somewhere to save details of specific brews and beans you've enjoyed

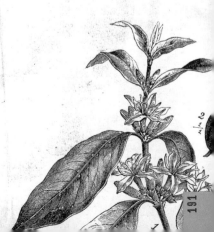

INDEX